I want to have

GW00371150

What early readers of the manuscript have said about
I want to have a Baby?

When debating the prospect of of motherhood, women
tend to soak up as much information as they can – from
friends who have been there, magaines and now books.
The fact that there has never been a book like this one is
one of its strongest selling points. There are things which
I didn't previously know, and wish that I had beforehand.
Emma Whyman

This book is full of the things that no one ever tells you
before you have a baby. I am a working mother of two
and I wish I'd known many of these facts before I started
my family!
Monisha Bharadwaj

I really enjoyed reading this book which is packed with
useful information for everyone, from those thinking about
a first baby to people like me with a second on the way.
Susan Morony

I must say how much I have enjoyed reading this book. I
really do feel it is something that has been missing from
the market and I am sure that many people will find it
extremely useful.
Anne Newman

Should be compulsory reading for all parents-to-be. We
didn't think twice before we had Joe – now we would!
Heidi Baker

Dr Sarah Brewer is a qualified doctor. Her major passion is writing and she now successfully combines both her careers through medical journalism. She writes regularly for a variety of publications, including *Top Santé*, *Woman's Weekly*, *Sugar*, *Parents* and *Pregnancy & Birth*. She is the author of several books, including *Planning a Baby – Preconceptual Care* (purely a health book), *The Complete Book of Men's Health* and *Super Baby*.

I want to have a Baby?

Dr Sarah Brewer

KYLE CATHIE LIMITED

Dedicated to all potential parents, everywhere, who
are in for one of the greatest shocks of their life when they
become a parent one day.
May that experience be everything
they wished for – and more.

Acknowledgements
I would like to thank everyone – individuals and organisations – who so kindly donated their
time and thoughts to provide the excellent, thought-provoking quotes throughout *I want to
have a Baby?* There simply isn't room to thank you all by name, but you know who you are.
But special thanks from the author and the publisher must go to Jane Balaskas, John Bell,
Dr Alex Bobak, Marion Braithwaite, Simon Brett, Marjorie Burke, Siobhan Carolan, Leigh
Chambers, Edward Chitham, Dr Carol Cooper, Professor John A Davies, Joy Dickens, Dr Rob
Hicks, the Kahlil Gibran Society, New York, Liz Kawonza, Macmillan Publishers, Dr Patricia
Macnair, Suzannah Olivier, Jill Palmer, Dr Bashir Qureshi, Susan Rice, Lisa Saffron,
Samantha Sherratt, Patricia Swanton, Virago Press, Dr Ann Whitehead and Emma Whyman.

First published in Great Britain in 1999 by
Kyle Cathie Limited
20 Vauxhall Bridge Road
London SW1V 2SA

ISBN 1 85626 299 5

Text © 1999 Dr Sarah Brewer
Editor: Kate Oldfield
Copy editor: Ann Newman
Typesetting: Heidi Baker

Dr Sarah Brewer is hereby identified as the author of this work in accordance with Section 77 of the
Copyright, Designs and Patents Act 1988

A CIP catalogue record for this title is available from the British Library

Printed and bound in Singapore by Kyodo Printing Co. Pte. Ltd.

The contents of this book are for information only and are not intended to be a
substitute for taking proper medical advice and should not be relied upon in this
way. Always consult a qualified doctor or health practitioner. The author and
publisher cannot accept responsibility for illness arising out of the failure to seek
medical advice from a doctor.

contents

Introduction 6

Chapter 1   The Reality: What having a baby entails. 9
Chapter 2   Potential Motherhood 25
Chapter 3   Potential Fatherhood 37
Chapter 4   Looking Ahead: To work or not to work 53
Chapter 5   Domestic Support Structures 76
Chapter 6   Financial Implications of Having a Baby. . . . 86
Chapter 7   Legal Implications of Having a Baby. 98
Chapter 8   Your Health Before You Conceive 113
Chapter 9   The Conception 137
Chapter 10   Pregnancy. 154
Chapter 11   Options for Birth 168
Chapter 12   The Early Days 179
Chapter 13   Special Cases 197
Chapter 14   The Future 216
Conclusion. 227

Appendices   i What Newcomers to Britain Need
                to Know about Having a Baby. 228
             ii Trade Secrets 234
             iii Resources 235
             Index 252

Introduction

If you are reading this book, then at some time or another, you have thought 'I want to have a baby(?)'. The question mark is all-important, and those six little words before it represent a variety of emotions for different people. For some it is a simple mission statement. For others, it may be a rhetorical question, an idle musing, a tentative exploratory quip or a deeply philosophical, internal debate.

When reading *I want to have a Baby?*, you may just be flirting with what sounds like a good idea, or may seriously be considering parenthood as an option for the near future. You may be in a stable relationship – heterosexual or gay – or be single and relatively free of emotional encumbrances. You may be approaching the top of your career ladder and thinking 'What next?' or just starting your chosen occupation and wondering how to build in the flexibility needed to accommodate a baby – one day.

Having a baby is one of the most profound rites of passage you will ever experience, for the transition from childlessness to parenthood inevitably turns your life upside-down. However much you promise that your lifestyle won't change, it *will*. It has to, for instead of being a single person, or one half of an independent couple, you are suddenly so much more. You are the mother, or father, of a tiny, vulnerable infant who is totally dependent – in mind, body and spirit – on *you*.

Nothing can completely prepare you for the immense impact a newborn will have on your life, but *I want to have a Baby?* aims to make your miracle less of a total shock. It is not just another baby book, but a book everyone should read if they feel they might like to have a baby ... one day. Read it before you conceive, or father, a child: few people realize the full implications of indulging one of their most basic urges – that of procreation.

I want to have a Baby? breaks the taboos surrounding the most ancient of female desires by daring to admit what often remains unsaid, and by delivering the hard-hitting facts about babies. Pondering the idea of having a baby, you may find yourself asking some rather soul-searching questions:

- Am I ready to be a parent?
- What does having a baby really entail?
- When is the right time?
- What about preconceptual care?
- What effects will pregnancy have on my health?
- How are we going to cope?
- How much does having a baby cost – financially, physically and emotionally?
- What are the legal implications?
- Who is going to look after my child?
- Should I return to work when my baby is born?
- Should I stay at home and look after my child myself?
- What if I smoke, drink alcohol or use recreational drugs?
- What if my fertility or my partner's is low?

All these questions – and more – may be running through your mind. Those in less usual situations may have other more difficult questions to consider:

- If I don't have a partner, should I still become a parent on my own – and if so, how?
- What are the implications if I'm gay? How do I find out about self-insemination?
- What if I have a long-term health problem, or am taking medication?

I want to have a Baby? is a compilation of orthodox and alternative voices that describes many aspects of having a baby you may not have considered before. The range of subjects covered stretches from childcare, financial planning and your legal responsibilities as a parent through to infertility treatment and gay parenting.

There are regular contributions throughout the book from Lisa Saffron, a lesbian mother with a daughter conceived by self-insemination. She has been active in promoting lesbian and gay parenthood since the 1980s, particularly through her books (*Challenging Conceptions – Planning a Family by Self-Insemination*, Cassell, 1994 and *What About the Children? Sons and Daughters of Lesbian and Gay Parents Speak About their Lives*, Cassell, 1996). She also writes regularly for a variety of publications and gives lectures on the subject of self-insemination and lesbian motherhood.

I want to have a Baby? is filled with startling facts – did you know for example that:

- women who have been on the pill for many years may have been conserving their best eggs
- every female is born with around 2 million eggs, but by the age of puberty only half a million remain
- eggs continue to be lost at a rate of over 1,000 per cycle
- the average chance of conceiving is only around 20 percent per month of trying
- once released, an egg can only be fertilized within 24-48 hours
- a quarter of all women experience some form of reduced fertility – 1 in 8 while trying for their first baby.

These facts and many more, along with a great deal of valuable information ensure that this book is essential reading for anyone who is a potential parent.

Chapter 1:
The Reality: What having a baby entails

A 1994 survey found that 77 percent of women aged 18-24 planned to start a family at some stage in their life, while 55 percent of those aged 25-34 who already had children wanted at least one more. Even among women over the age of 35, 8 percent still dreamed of hearing the patter of tiny feet. Whether you know now that you definitely want to have a baby, are ambivalent, or cringe at the mere thought, this book is written for you.

Having children is a major priority for couples. However, it is all too easy to enter the mystical realm of parenthood with little consideration for the impact a baby will have on your life. Many people spend more time and effort on planning to buy a house than they do when deciding to have a baby. It is estimated that one in three babies is unplanned, yet the most critical time of your baby's development is the first few weeks of gestation – often before the mother is even aware that she is pregnant. By posing your questions and worries about parenthood in advance, you can formulate a game plan and organize your finances, career, relationship, domestic arrangements, contraception and preconceptual care around your decision to have a baby – or not.

What is a baby?

A popular definition describes a baby as a creature producing loud noises at one end and streams of unpleasantness at the other. The key to being a good parent is in deciding which end is which and where to put the nappy and the teat. At the same time babies do have universal appeal. They are artfully designed to tug at your heart strings and elicit instinctive parenting responses with just a flicker of a smile, a fleeting glance, and a mere gurgle or a coo. They are

I've always loved other people's children but never realized how much more I would love my own. Life would no longer seem complete without them. Jane

I never played with dolls as a child and have always known I didn't want to have a baby. Having seen what happens to friends who become parents has strengthened my feelings. They descend into the parenthood trap, from which there seems little chance of escape. I need my freedom. Zandra

I didn't have a clue what to expect – I was used to babies who could sit up, crawl or even feed themselves. I'd never seen a newborn before. He seemed so fragile and helpless, I wanted to hand him back. I was so afraid I was going to hurt him. Tom

equipped with the ultimate 'aaah!' factor, for just the sight, sound, feel and smell of a baby can stimulate the immediate interaction of hormones, pheromones, primitive nerve pathways and higher centres of the brain. Even if other people's babies have only a weak effect, your own will undoubtedly knock you for six. Women are biologically programmed to develop an unconditional love for their baby and an overwhelming need to nurture and protect. This is not surprising, for reproduction is essential for the survival of our species and the quality and diversity of the human gene pool.

Some people seem to over-ride their procreational urges, or never to have acquired them.

Never is a dangerous word when it comes to potential parenthood, however. One minute you may happily believe your childless life is complete when out of the blue – and with no discernible trigger – something clicks and the desire to have a baby becomes so overwhelming and intense it is impossible to ignore. Wanting to have a baby, quite simply, is one of the main reasons for existence.

What is it like to be a parent?

Until you become a parent, it is difficult to imagine how much your life will shift out of orbit. Instead of revolving around you, or you and your partner, there is suddenly a new kingpin to your existence.

Many parents find the first few months harder than they expected. After the excitement of actually seeing your baby for the first time, comes the reality of sleepless nights, physical exhaustion and seemingly endless feeds, nappy changes and laundry.

When you have your first baby, your life changes for ever as you can't do anything on impulse. James

I've always coped with everything life threw my way, so I naturally assumed I'd cope with having a baby. After all, how could something so tiny and helpless manage to change my life? Big shock. Having a baby wasn't like having a pet or ordering a new appliance. I wasn't prepared for the enormous demands on my time, energy, emotions, finances – all my resources in fact. If I could put the clock back, I sometimes think I might not have had him. But then again, I feel so proud whenever I realize I am a mother. Catherine

If you have envisaged a baby who dutifully sleeps through the night and smiles happily between colic-free feeds with little energy wasted in crying, think again. Such babies are few and far between. The reality can be terrifying. Most babies don't sleep through the night for at least the first three months – and often much longer.

> I always saw childbirth as the big hurdle in having a baby. But it was nothing compared with the physical, mental and emotional rollercoaster that followed as I tried to cope with my newborn child. Nothing and no one prepared me for the amazing impact a baby would have on our lives. The exhaustion was the worst. I wanted to crawl away and cry. Sonia

Different people have different expectations and experiences, but being a parent is a great social equalizer. Being a mother gives women from different backgrounds something in common, and more to discuss, than those who are from their own social sphere but childless. For being a parent exposes you to a whole new spectrum of emotions – love, fear, hope, concern and joy – which, instead of being centred around yourself, are projected forwards on to another human being. Part of you is now living for, and through, your offspring. It brings home the fleeting nature of life, and its inevitable cycles of birth, maturation, reproduction and demise.

> I never dreamed it was possible to love someone or something so much it physically hurt. I literally ache at the thought of my baby suffering harm. Lucy

> I spent the whole of the first year of my baby's life worrying about cot death. I didn't let him out of my sight. He slept in our bed between us at night, and during the day he slept in my arms, or in his buggy in a quiet corner of the kitchen where I could keep an eye on him. Only when he was 12 months old did we feel confident enough to move him into his own room. We used two baby-listening devices though. Just in case. Sarah

One of the biggest changes is the way being a parent affects your adult relationships and the way in which friends, family and colleagues perceive you. Some changes are positive, but others are inevitably negative. In one fell swoop, you've converted your parents into grandparents, your brothers and sisters into uncles or aunts and shifted the balance of inheritance in your family. This may not matter, but in some cases it is a crucial factor in the disintegration of a family, especially if your partner already has children from a previous relationship.

While I was expecting, I remained the centre of attention until my baby was born. She then stole the stage and I was displaced to the wings. At least, that's what it seemed like. My husband felt the same, except his marginalization started seven months earlier when I first announced I was pregnant. I think we both secretly resented Jessica a little, though we'd never admit that publicly, and especially not to each other. Anna

Before I was a parent, hearing about senseless tragedies such as a child's murder and the deaths at Dunblane made me feel numb but didn't really affect me personally. Now I have a baby, I shed real tears whenever I hear of a child's death. I know what it's really like to be a parent, and I can imagine the grief of another parent's loss. Kate

If I had to give one tip to anyone thinking about having a baby, it's this: don't give so much of your life away to your baby that you have nothing left for yourself. Be a little selfish. Have at least one night off a week in which you both go down the pub, see friends or have a romantic meal for two. It's vital to keep your relationship together. John

I sometimes wonder whether it was a good idea to bring a child into a world where so many are starving or intent on killing each other. Simon

I love my children, I'd die for them, but if I could have my life over again I wouldn't have had them. J

While becoming a parent will bond you closer to friends who already have children, those who are childless – whether consciously or otherwise – will frequently drift away. You can no longer drop everything and race down the pub, off to a football match, grab tickets for a concert or even go out for a meal without a certain amount of forethought.

Like most parents-to-be, we blithely promised the baby would change nothing, have absolutely no effect on our lifestyle. We'd continue going out to eat, the theatre, seeing friends and most of all, we wouldn't bore everyone to death with stories of first smiles and tales of nappies. We both work from home and thoughtit would be easy. We didn't go out for six months. We didn't have the energy or the inclination. And yes, our conversations did all revolve round the baby. She took over our lives. Joanne and Nick

One of the biggest adjustments for those in a stable relationship, is learning to share your partner with your baby and vice versa. The physical and emotional demands of having a baby often mean you suddenly have less time for your partner – and certainly much less time alone.

I sometimes wish I'd never had my baby. I love him dearly, but he had a devastating effect on my life and indirectly led to the break-up of our marriage.
I developed severe postnatal depression, and my husband couldn't cope with the fact that *I* suddenly couldn't cope. He'd never seen me like that before. Alison

Not only will your lifestyle and relationships change, but becoming a parent alters your outlook on life, too. You may find yourself philosophizing about the state of the world or being more conscious of the environment, for by having a baby you have suddenly acquired an emotional, as well as a genetic, investment in the future.

Becoming a parent meant I suddenly couldn't read or listen to news stories about children. I remember switching off a horror film in which a couple let a strange child they found in their garden sleep in the same room as their newborn baby. I could just imagine what was going to happen next and I couldn't bear it. Sarah

The biological clock is ticking

Unlike men, women have the additional pressure when wanting to have a baby, of a limited time span in which to do it. Many women choose to hit the snooze button on their biological clock, but just how long can you afford to put child-bearing off? When can you realistically expect to hit the menopause?

Every female is born with around 2 million eggs in her ovaries. By the time she has her first period however, only half a million eggs remain. The rest have slowly disappeared through a natural process of reabsorption. The number of eggs dwindles further as egg follicles continue to break down or stop responding to hormone signals at a rate of 1,000-1,500 per month. An average of 15 eggs also start developing each month, although only one is usually mature enough to be released at ovulation – the others are reabsorbed. Eventually, the menopause is triggered when only a few thousand egg follicles remain. These are unable to produce enough oestrogen to control the monthly cycle so menstruation stops and fertility comes to a close.

For most women, their last natural period occurs between the ages of 45 and 55, the average being around 51 years. Some women find that their menopause occurs earlier than expected however. When menopause occurs before the age of 45, it is classed as premature.

A natural premature menopause affects 1-2 percent of women. A further 8 percent have an early menopause as a result of medical or surgical treatment. Overall, as many as one in ten women may enter the menopause before the age of 45 and thus experience an unexpectedly early end to their fertility. (For more information on premature menopause see chapter 13.)

Important questions to ask

To be in the best position to decide whether or not you want to have a baby, one day, you need to analyse your feelings by asking a series of questions under the general headings of: Why? When? Who? How? What? Where? and How Much? It is also worth considering What if? for a baby does not come with a guarantee, any more than it arrives with an owner's manual. It's one thing planning to have a normal pregnancy and healthy baby, but how will you cope if something goes wrong?

Having children evokes depths of feelings I was not aware of before. Joy, anger, surprise, all somehow exaggerated. Motherhood is a very precious experience and one to treasure because before you know it there's a flutter of wings and they've gone for ever. Things will never be the same again. Pat

I experienced a premature menopause at the age of 33 – just when I was thinking of having a baby. I couldn't believe it. It just seemed so unfair. I'd say to anyone putting off having a family – don't do it, you may miss the boat. Joan

I didn't think I had any maternal feelings until the baby was actually here. But from the moment Katy arrived, I adored her. Cecilia

Never, never have children to try and mend a relationship. Children, from the moment of birth, are the most demanding things, both physically and psychologically. I didn't know I could shout until I had children! So far from mending a relationship that is already fragile, it is much more likely to break it. Pat

Why?

There are many different reasons why you may want to have a baby – some are positive while others are deeply negative:

I decided to have a baby because I needed someone all of my own to love. Annie, single parent

I had a baby in an attempt to mend our marriage after discovering my husband had had an affair. After finding out I was pregnant, I read in a magazine that 40 percent of men are unfaithful to their wives while she is expecting and became hysterical. The marriage finally floundered after our daughter was born. Julia

While your reasons for wanting to become a parent may seem valid, take a little time to think them through to ensure you are having a baby for the right reasons, for you. People often decide to have a baby because:

- they want to fulfil deep maternal or paternal urges
- it's something they've always wanted to do
- they feel incomplete without one
- they want to seal their love for each other
- there's nothing else to do
- they've done everything else and are wondering what to try next
- it seems like a good idea
- it's expected of them
- their partner desperately wants one
- it's something everyone does, isn't it?
- they want to rescue a relationship
- they want to escape from a particular situation
- they want to prove that they're fertile
- someone else has just had one, and they feel left out
- they feel a need for revenge
- they hope to solidify their position
- they think it will secure their inheritance
- they want to pass on their genes
- their biological clock is ticking.

When?

You may feel that it's never the right or wrong time to have a baby. It may seem difficult to fit one in because you are too busy, too young, too old, too poor, insecure, have not yet found the right partner or are in a relationship that society frowns on.

The right time to have a baby is when you feel able to offer a child an upbringing that is stable, loving and secure. Only you can decide when that time has arrived, but a number of questions need to be asked (and these will be examined in more detail in the chapters that follow):

- Are you in a stable, loving relationship?
- Are you living in suitable accommodation?
- Are you financially secure?
- Is your income guaranteed?
- What if you were to give up work or go part-time rather than full-time?
- Are you eligible for paid maternity leave/allowance?
- Are you and your partner in good physical and mental health?
- Are you emotionally ready to become a parent?
- Are you eating a nutritious, healthy, wholefood diet?
- Have you and your partner followed a preconceptual programme, including stopping smoking, avoiding alcohol, avoiding over-the-counter drugs and only taking essential medications?
- Have you been taking folic acid supplements to help reduce the risk of neural tube defects such as spina bifida?
- Have you got out of your system all the things you know will be difficult once you have a child (...backpacking in Nepal, or dog-sledding in Greenland)?

Many women who know they would like to have a baby one day assume this will probably be when they are settled and – probably – married. In 1996 however, 35.8 percent of all births in the UK (equivalent to 232,521 children) took place outside of marriage. So-called illegitimacy is no longer a stigma, and many women feel that marriage is no longer therefore a requisite for having a baby. Sadly however, in 1997, around 9,000 girls under the age of 16 became pregnant, half of whom decided to have a termination of pregnancy.

Maternity leave

When choosing the right time to have a baby, one of the factors you may want to consider is your eligibility for maternity leave. Before getting pregnant, it is worth reading your Staff Handbook, Contract

I don't think there is ever a 'right' time to have a baby, still less a right interval between children. There will always be drawbacks to the first baby – loss of income if the wife is working, alarm (possibly) at the prospect of this unknown new way of life, change in the dynamics of the marriage ... But I am *immeasurably* glad to have had them. Cecilia

I wasn't ready to have a baby until my late thirties. As a result, I deliberately avoided playing coochie-coo with other people's babies as I was increasingly irritated by nudges and winks accusing me of being broody and wanting to be next. Alison

My advice is that at the very least, you should have a decent interval (say two years) between your children, so the first is walking when you have the next. Our daughter is three years older than her brother, and they have always got along together very well. Dalma

of Employment or the Maternity Information Pack provided by your employer to see what maternity leave you are entitled to, and the policy regarding return to work. By timing your pregnancy carefully, you may be able to increase the amount of maternity leave, and maternity pay, you are entitled to (see chapters 4 and 7).

When we first decided to have a baby, I realized that if I got pregnant straight away, I would miss out on extended maternity leave. I wouldn't have been continuously employed for 23 months at the time of departure, which had to be between 11 and 4 weeks before the expected date of birth. We therefore waited another 8 weeks before trying to conceive. Just as well – I fell pregnant straight away. That simple decision earned us several thousand pounds. Lucy

Planning second or subsequent pregnancies

If you already have a child, this may play a part in your decision about when to have another. Some parents decide to have their children very close together, so their offspring can be playmates. Others feel a longer gap in between is more appropriate.

My first son was born when I was thirty-seven. We wanted to have a second child, and as it became obvious very early on that William was a pretty strong and determined character, it seemed the sooner another baby was introduced into the household the better. Apart from the fact that we felt that it would be good for him, I also thought that it might be easier, in the long run, to deal with all the young baby work in a relatively short period of time and get it over with. Charlie was born 15 months later. It's harder work than I anticipated dealing with two such young children, but the big bonus is that William loves Charlie (also a determined character) and he won't remember a time when he ruled the roost on his own. We also think – and hope – that as they are so close together in age they will be able to be good friends as well as brothers. Susie

Although some people prefer to have their children as close together as possible, others disagree. If you leave too long a gap between your children, however, people may misinterpret this and make insensitive comments.

When I was pregnant for the third time, several people unthinkingly said to me, 'Oh, it must be a mistake.' It wasn't. Our third baby was very planned and very wanted. Then it was 'Oh, you must be wanting a little girl' as we already had two boys. My reply was, 'No, whatever comes will be loved and wanted.' Then, unbelievably, people would say, 'Oh, silly me. Of course. You must be a Catholic!' We are not. We just wanted a big family, and it was nobody else's business but our own. Charlotte

You therefore need to weigh up how you would ideally like your family to be spaced, but be flexible – conceptions rarely go according to plan.

Who?

One of the most important considerations is who (if anyone) will be co-parent of your child? Questions to ask yourself are:

- Do you have a stable relationship with a partner?
- Does the nature of your relationship mean you will need access to donor sperm? (See The Conception: Gay parenting, chapter 9.)
- Do you need to consider who will be birth parents and who will be legal parents in the case of surrogacy?
- Who do you turn to for help if you wish to adopt or foster a child?
- Who will be guardian of your child in the event of your death?
- Who can you turn to for help if you decide to have a child on your own, or if you unexpectedly become a single parent?

How?

Many people assume that when they want to have a baby, they just throw away the contraception and will quickly conceive. It isn't always that simple, however. The fertile period of a woman's menstrual cycle is relatively short. Once released, an egg only remains capable of fertilization for 24-48 hours. Sperm can survive inside the female reproductive tract for around five days and have been found alive up to seven days after sex, although whether or not they are still capable of penetrating an egg after this time is unknown. You need to know the best times to make love in any month to optimize your chances of success. The average chance of conceiving is at least 20 percent per month and most couples will achieve their target within one year. That said, however, infertility is the the most common reason for referral to hospital in people under

A professional says ...

Imagine two couples who both have a child adamant they are not having a second. Why? Well, the first couple have had the 'perfect child' and are convinced there is no way another could be so perfect, so it's best not to have another. The second couple's experience has been horrendous so there's no way they are risking going through that again.

Dr Rob Hicks, GP

the age of 40. One in 20 males are subfertile at any one time and a quarter of all women will experience some form of reduced fertility – one in eight while trying for their first baby. Overall, 3 percent of women are involuntarily childless and 6 percent are unable to have as many children as they would wish.

Once you decide the time is right to try for a baby, you will need to find the time – and energy – to fit the conception into your routine. It is not always easy for a couple to get together during the woman's most fertile time, and if you will be using donated sperm, you'll need to arrange to get to the clinic or meet with a donor for self-insemination when you are at your most fertile. Questions you may need to ask include:

- How will you fit a(nother) baby into your life?
- How do you calculate your most fertile period?
- How do you use an ovulation predictor kit?
- When and how often should you make love?
- How can you tell when you're pregnant?
- What if you don't get pregnant straight away?
- How long do you wait before seeking help if you fail to conceive?
- How successful are assisted conception techniques?
- How do you go about adopting a child?
- How are you going to cope?
- How will you balance the conflicting demands of parenthood, a career and other personal goals?
- Can you really provide the foundations of future success for the life you hope to create?
- If you are in a gay relationship, are you able to arrange insemination from a suitable donor?

What?

There are a number of considerations to include under the general heading of 'What?':

- What is it like to be pregnant?
- What adverse effects could pregnancy have on you?
- At what stage do you start taking maternity leave?
- What is it like to give birth naturally or via Caesarean?
- What are the pros and cons of breast or bottle feeding?
- What are the domestic implications of having a baby?
- What are the legal implications of having a baby?

- What are your rights as a parent?
- What effect will a new baby have on existing children in our family?

Speak to as many people as possible who have had children – friends, family, work colleagues, neighbours, to find out what effects a baby had on their life. Encourage them to be honest. People who do not know you well may give you a glossy, cornflake-packet-family account of parenthood, but what you want to know about is the reality – warts and all.

Where?

When planning to have a baby, you may need to think ahead to the time of birth:

- Where do you want to have your child – at home or in hospital?
- What options are available?
- Are you likely to be living abroad at the time? If so, how sophisticated are the provisions there for childbirth?
- Do you want to move so you are closer to friends, family, work, amenities or childcare provisions?

How much?

Babies are expensive. Obviously you want the best you can afford for your offspring, but how much is that likely to be? Ask yourself:

- How much do *first* babies really cost?
- How can I plan ahead financially?
- What insurance plans are available?
- Does everything have to be brand new; would I have easy access to hand-me-downs?

With my first baby we couldn't afford to have everything new. I shopped carefully at good-quality second-hand stores and made use of hand-me-downs from my sister who insisted on buying everything new for her own children. Only the Moses basket and cot mattress were bought new along with a few early baby clothes that I couldn't resist. With our second baby, we have a lot more cash to spare: as so many items originally used with Josh were still fine our second baby was also a 'second-hand' child. Julie

I don't see the point in buying expensive baby clothes – they grow out of them so quickly. Parveet

For me, part of the fun of having a baby is personally selecting the outfits she will wear. I wouldn't dream of wearing second-hand myself and therefore don't think I should lower my standards for my baby. Selina

Becoming a single mum seemed glamorous until our school arranged for fifth formers to care for a virtual baby over a weekend. We all agreed we would be more careful with contraception in future. Tina

What if?

It's worth giving a thought to how you would cope with a situation where things did not go according to plan. What would happen if:

- you conceived a multiple pregnancy – twins, triplets or more
- you had a difficult pregnancy and could not work
- your baby was born very prematurely and was in a Special Care Baby Unit
- your child was born with a congenital abnormality, or developed a life-threatening or life-limiting illness
- you needed to consider a termination of pregnancy
- you had an attack of genital herpes at the time your baby is due to be born
- you or your partner were diagnosed with a serious illness before you became pregnant or during/after the pregnancy?

Reality check

For those who really want to experience first-hand what it is like to have a crying, demanding newborn baby at home there is always the Baby Think It Over: a life-size, plastic virtual baby that cries every few hours, requires constant attention and registers neglect and abuse. The crying goes on for a realistic amount of time and is stopped by inserting a special key in the baby's back and applying pressure until it stops, which can take up to 30 minutes.

> **I thought I wanted to be a parent, but having a Baby Think It Over in the house for three days put me off wanting to have children for at least another five years.** Sean

While virtual babies are useful for illustrating the reality behind the idyllic image of a cooing baby, it is important to stress that no one should base their decision on whether or not to have a baby on their experiences with an artificial one. It is far better to spend some time with a real baby belonging to a relative or friend, and to talk to as many parents of new babies as you possibly can.

A professional on ...
What potential parents should be aware of before having a baby

'**W**hen I grow up I am going to have six children.' Childhood fantasies of being a mummy and a daddy are a part of most children's growing up. Dolls do not cry at night – it is all part of playing at being grown-ups.

As we grow up we may continue to have our fantasies of being a perfect parent, with a perfect child, a fantasy fed into by the media portrayal of happy babies wearing Huggies or eating Heinz baby food.

Becoming a parent is a special and life-changing experience, which can be enhanced by some careful consideration and awareness, ahead of time, of some of the issues, changes and challenges that can be involved.

The Vernon Family Project is a joint venture between Spurgeon's Child Care – a Christian organization set up to support family life and provide positive experiences for children – and the Vernon Baptist Church in King's Cross, London. Those working with the project have a great deal of experience on aspects people could consider before embarking on parenthood as there are many less obvious aspects of being a mum or dad that not everyone thinks about in advance. Marion Braithwaite, the Family Project Manager, offers the following advice:

What previous experience have you had with babies and children? Have you been an older brother or sister, an auntie or uncle, or worked with children? Experience helps with knowing the basics such as bathing and nappy changing and reduces anxiety levels. It may not, however, prepare you for the 24 hour dependence of a small baby. Some parents are pleasantly surprised at how well their baby sleeps, eats, etc. Many however, are not prepared for the all day and all night shifts that can occur. Have you planned and prepared to share the night shift? How can you catch up during the day? Prior consideration of these issues will help in coping with the temporary difficulties that arise through lack of routine and lack of sleep in the early weeks of parenthood. Building a good and trusting relationship with your GP and health visitor will provide a ready source of helpful advice and support.

What can you reasonably expect of your child, at what stage? Some previous knowledge of child development may prevent a great deal of heartache when your child does not do what you, or your relatives and friends, think the child should be doing. When should your baby have its first tooth, hold a pencil, speak in sentences, have road sense? There is a spectrum of child development and circumstances that may cause variations. Being forearmed with information can put these things in their proper perspective.

What can you expect of yourself? No parent is perfect – expect to feel angry and frustrated at times. Think of ways of dealing with it. How do you deal with those sorts of feelings now? Can these means be transferred to a child care situation? You may not immediately bond with your child. Give yourself time and be kind to yourself.

Are there cultural issues to take into account? Recognise them, value the differences. Consider how you will help and support your child in enjoying their heritage and managing society. Be aware that there may be cultural aspects of family traditions that are at variance with the society in which you live.

Marion Braithwaite, Family Project Manager: Spurgeon's Child Care, The Vernon Family Project

A professional on ...
A child needs two parents

Being a parent can be a wonderful experience, being a child can be a wonderful experience. However a child needs the love and support of both parents. It needs the right to the respect of both parents, and it needs to be listened to by both parents. If it loses any of these, it can have a disastrous childhood. The following poem written at the beginning of this century by Kahlil Gibran, the well-known poet from the Middle East, sums up the message we would like to pass to all parents.

'On Children' [1]

They are the sons and daughters of Life's longings for itself.

They came through you but not from you,

And though they are with you yet they belong not to you.

You may give them your love but not your thoughts,

For they have their own thoughts.

You may house their bodies but not their souls,

For their souls dwell in the house of tomorrow, which you cannot visit, not even in your dreams.

You may strive to be like them, but seek not to make them like you,

For life goes not backward nor tarries with yesterday.

You are the bows from which your children as living arrows are sent forth.

The poem needs careful reading, and on each reading a new message comes across, but the overall message is that you should not use children to hurt others, because ultimately you will hurt the children and they in turn can hurt and reject you.

John Bell, Co-director, Both Parents Forever

---

[1] 'On Children', by Kahlil Gibran, from *The Prophet*, 1923.

Gay parenting: The reality
by **Lisa Saffron**

Deciding whether or not to become a parent if you are in a gay relationship is fraught with even wider considerations than those for traditional male-female parents. As well as planning to cope with the changes the baby itself will bring, you will also have to prepare yourself for the judgmental attitudes and prejudices of a large section of the population. If the urge to have a baby is strong enough, your relationship is stable, and the time is right, however, the odds do not have to be insurmountable.

When *is* the right time for a gay couple to have a baby? Toni, 45, is the lesbian mother of a 13-year-old daughter:

I chose to get pregnant on my own when I was in my early thirties. It was the right time and I don't regret it but it was not the ideal time. Ideally I wanted to share parenting with a partner but I had little confidence in my ability to form a secure, long-term relationship. I was in a rocky relationship with a woman at the time I made the decision to have a baby, but we split up when I was pregnant. I felt that if I postponed the baby until after the right woman came along, and after we had established ourselves as a couple, I might well be into the menopause. It wasn't until my daughter Claire was five and a half that I met Theresa, fell in love with her and set up home with her. We've now been a family for nearly eight years and I no longer think of myself as a single mother.

Karen, 32, is in a lesbian relationship and trying to get pregnant:

We've been together for seven years and we feel stronger than ever in our relationship. The time is right now to have children. For the first couple of years we were travelling, but since we came back and bought a house and settled down, having a baby has become a realistic thing to do. We have a core of supportive friends which is important as well.

Chapter 2:
Potential Motherhood

Being a mother is one of the most fulfilling experiences a woman can have. No one can prepare you for the range of emotions you will feel when holding your baby in your arms for the first time. You may feel a great, heart-wrenching intensity of love for the tiny bundle squinting up at you. You may feel an enormous need to protect the vulnerable, fragile life. You may feel more needed, worthwhile and necessary than ever before. Alternatively, you may just feel numb – still in shock from the primitive process you have endured to bring your baby into the world.

> I knew it was going to happen, but there is a great gulf between the nine months you spend looking forward to your baby during pregnancy, and the barbaric process of giving birth. Thank God for the epidural. But the reality of holding your own baby to your breast takes all memories of pain and sweat away. The change from anonymous bump to real, breathing, living, separate person was a complete miracle. Kate

The bond between mother and baby, and the love you feel for your offspring is uniquely strong. Even the most passive woman will feel an aggressive need to protect her young.

> I did not know the absolute power in which I would be held, regarding the maternal instinct. It is the strangest force above any other consideration. I would fight anyone, anywhere, any time, with my bare hands if needs be, to protect my children. Linda

> I thought I wanted children but was never very sure why. I wasn't the maternal type. Other people's children induced feelings ranging from horror to disgust. I had no desire to kiss or cuddle friends'

I wish I had known in advance how painful it can be for me when my son hurts. He has just had brain surgery and I nearly had a nervous breakdown. I would do anything to stop him from having to go through hurt, physical or mental, again. Annie babies, with their streams of glop and snot, and stale musty smells. The night before my first child was born (I was booked in for an elective Caesarean so I knew it was my last day of freedom!) I had a huge panic attack. It all seemed to be a terrible mistake. What the hell had we done? Was this the end of life as we knew it? What about my career, holidays, expensive shopping habits ... ? But as soon as Charlotte was nestled in my arms, deep maternal instincts and love welled up from some previously dormant part of my brain. I instantly knew that we had done the most brilliant thing and that everything would all be all right.

The strange thing is that three years later I went through exactly the same panic (having re-established career, holidays and shopping). But again there was exactly the same relief and instinctive knowing when Rory arrived. I still don't care much for other people's children (apologies to all my friends here) but mine are just scrumptious.
Patricia, doctor

Deep maternal feelings can take time to develop, however. Not every new mother loves her baby unconditionally immediately – it can (and often does) take time for the relationship to grow. Many women recovering from the delivery of a longed-for baby are shocked at feelings of numbness and an inability to conjure up instant feelings of love for their newborn infant. This is quite normal, especially if you are exhausted from the delivery – the baby can seem like an anticlimax.

You have to get to know your baby and come to terms with reality. It takes time for love to grow. At this stage your baby may seem more like a screaming banshee keeping you from some well-earned sleep than a person deserving of your instant affection. You may even resent the baby initially if the birth was more uncomfortable or physically exhausting than you had imagined it would be. Again, this is not uncommon. Within a few weeks, however, the baby will usually have you enthralled, although if you develop postnatal depression this can severely interfere with the bonding process (see chapter 12).

How motherhood changes your life

Babies have a way of taking over your life – domestic, personal and social. When you become a mother, your whole world will start to revolve around infants, and not just your own.

When I bravely escaped to Edinburgh for a weekend reunion with university contemporaries, filled with hope of stimulating intellectual conversation, what horror to find all talk centred on milk powder, breast-feeding and nappies and comparing baby notes. Elizabeth

While you may long for the company of childless friends in order to escape from the world of parenthood for a few precious hours, this becomes less and less easy.

Prior to our baby's arrival my husband and I were heavily involved in social and community activities. Shortly before the birth, I remember telling a committee member that we would resume our full involvement as soon as 'things returned to normal'. Our friend smiled knowingly and said, 'Things will never return to "normal" as you know it now'. She was right.

In the early months after the birth, I remember feeling utterly exhausted and emotionally drained at the end of each day. Yet, when my baby was finally asleep and I looked down at the cherubic face sleeping peacefully in his cot, feelings of exhaustion were replaced by a deep, protective love for him. Despite all the hard work involved in caring for a very demanding baby, I could not bring myself to hand him over to a childminder and return to the office. I was prepared to put my career on 'hold' to care for my baby full-time. I figured that the best investment I could ever make was the time I spent nurturing my young child.

Even so, there was a price to be paid for this decision — I lost touch with all my friends in the 'corporate' world. Our lifestyles were now worlds apart. Meanwhile, my new friends' eyes (i.e. the Toddler Group crowd) glazed over whenever I tried to talk about any issue other than nappies, toilet training and who had managed to feed solids to their baby first. There were days when I missed the stimulation of my former career. Marjorie

Social isolation can be even worse for a single mother, especially if there are few relatives or friends around who are able or willing to help. Even in these difficult circumstances however, the bond between mother and baby is powerfully strong — perhaps even more so if mother and child are all each other has in the world:

I've always been a single parent and deeply resent the negative stereotype portrayed by the government and media. It is damaging,

My biggest problem, possibly accentuated by having two little ones at the same stage, was a social one. The only people I could happily visit and who understood were those in similar small-child situations, which limited conversation. Invitations gleefully accepted to those unencumbered inevitably proved a nightmare: a trail of destruction by my two relatively 'good' children, and cat-on-hot-bricks feelings for me. At home, when one particular, child-hating friend arrived, the 'good' children immediately turned into monsters, clomping downstairs in my high-heeled shoes and being overpoweringly demanding, so that she doubted my fitness for motherhood. Elizabeth

A professional on ...
Your first baby

Having a first baby is the most emotional time in a woman's life without exception. Suddenly there is a tiny, helpless brand-new person who depends on you totally.

I spent the first few days in hospital proudly showing off my new daughter, accepting scores of congratulatory phone calls, opening hundreds of cards and receiving dozens of bouquets of flowers.

But the romance turns to reality once you get home. A baby is not a toy. It cannot be put away when you are fed up with it and want to do something else. It always wants feeding when you sit down to a meal, it always cries just as you are dropping off to sleep at night, it always demands attention when you are in the bath. And it takes up so much of your time.

At best your baby needs feeding every four hours, at worst every two. Then she is sick over everything. You are forced to walk around in old clothes that you can put in the wash every time your little one throws up on them – at least three times a day.

The first six weeks are the worst. You feel like a zombie, continually tired and unable to talk or think about nothing but baby.

In the dark nights as you sit alone trying to quieten a crying baby you feel lost, deserted, unloved. You wonder if you have done the right thing giving birth to this little bundle. But in the bright light of day when she smiles and chuckles you know that you have.

Once you have had your baby neither you nor your partner will ever be the same. You become totally emotionally involved with your new baby and experience feelings you never realized you had.

Jill Palmer, medical correspondent, *Daily Mirror*

and both untrue and unfair. My son and I are a family and a bloody good one. We don't like the constant undermining of our situation. Annie

Adjusting to motherhood

Adjusting to being a mother will take time. Looking after a baby is a full-time occupation which is suddenly thrust on you – one day you are lying down with your feet up doing relatively little, and choosing how to pass the time. The next, your whole life revolves around a new being and it is natural to resent this a little, especially when you are exhausted from lack of sleep and feel you have no quality time left for yourself or your partner. The early days will pass in a blur of chaos, confusion, trial, error and the implementation of a new daily pattern and routine. Where once you may have got up at a leisurely pace, you now have to fit in with your baby's sleep-wake cycle, and deal with his or her needs before you have time for your own. It is not unusual to suddenly realize you are still in your dressing-gown at lunch-time, having not had time even to think about getting dressed.

You may also be coping with baby blues or postnatal depression (see chapter 12). While initially there will be help at hand, perhaps in the form of your partner on paternity leave, the midwife, health visitor, mother or mother-in-law, there will soon come a time when much of this help tails off and you are suddenly on your own.

> As time passed, being a wife and mother was proving to be tiring and lonely. It was quite frightening when the health visitor stopped coming and I realised I was on my own with a baby. Jane

On the other hand:

> I couldn't wait for everyone to go away, stop interfering, and let me get on with caring for my baby. I didn't want anyone else around getting in the way. I spent hours playing with him, watching him sleep, lovingly ironing his clothes and taking him for walks in his mountain buggy. This was our special time for discovering each other – the best time of my life. Maria

No two babies are alike, however, and inevitably you will have different experiences with every baby you have.

Second time round it is so much easier. You've been through the culture shock, got used to handling the demands of a tiny baby, learned how they feed, why they cry and what can make them sleep. You've got all the right systems in place: the clothes, equipment, lists of babysitters ... You've learnt the tricks of the trade. In fact the hardest thing for us has been coping with the upset that the arrival of Rory has caused to his three-year-old sister. It's taken all our psychological wiles and deep cunning to deal with her regression back to a storming, tantrum-throwing psuedo-18-month-old, while Rory needs little more attention than a bag of sugar. Patricia, doctor

The experience you gain from a first child does not always mean you will know what to do with the next one. For us, having a second baby was very much more like having a first! Our first had been the most laid-back baby imaginable – she never cried, did everything like clockwork, and went completely by the book. It was only when the second came along that we found out what having a real baby was like! Anne

Family versus career

When deciding whether or not it is the right time to have children, you will need to consider the demands of your work. Being a parent and being an employee (or self-employed) are demanding occupations. Having to juggle job and family is a continuous problem for working women and finding a balance that suits everyone can often seem impossible. Any woman who works will have to consider which is her main priority.

On the one hand, careers may be potentially threatened (or the glass ceiling may appear to descend) once a baby is in the picture. On the other, spending all-important quality time with a family and watching children grow up, may be equally threatened by a career. Surveys suggest that four out of five women feel home should always come first, but only four in ten feel they get the balance right. More than half of working mothers feel that they are missing out on seeing their children grow up, and find that they regret the sacrifices they have made for their jobs. Even so, some mothers find that being able to escape to work from the constraints and daily stresses of motherhood is something that keeps them happy and sane.

Only you can decide which role – career woman, mother, or both – is right for you. Even if one particular option seems correct now, will it still be right in one years', five years' or ten years' time? One in ten working women admit to postponing or sacrificing their chance of being a mother in order to put their career first. In such cases there is also the question of the biological clock to consider (see chapters 1 and 13): how would you feel if you left it too late and could not get pregnant when you wished? While the development of assisted conception techniques make this less of a problem than it used to be, you must still consider whether you could live with that eventuality.

Not wanting to be a mother

If you do decide not to have children yet, you may have to deal with pressure from family and friends who can't seem to understand why you are still childless. For some women this becomes more and more of a problem, especially if they really do not want to become a parent. Just because everyone else seems either to have or want children does not mean that *you* have to. But if you make the decision not to have a baby you will need to be aware of the prejudices you may meet and the assumptions people will make about your fertility:

> I have never wanted to have children and decided that if it wasn't an issue for me, it shouldn't be for other people either. My decisions are my own business and no one else's. People assume I am infertile and I've found over the years that it is easier to foster this belief than to go into all the reasons why I chose not to procreate. Sian

Determining the sex

While medical techniques (and old wives' remedies) are available to help increase the chance of conceiving a girl or a boy, these are not foolproof, and medical procedures are only licensed to help reduce the risk of serious sex-linked conditions, not for producing a cosmetically desirable mix of offspring (see chapter 9). Even relying on information from an early ultrasound scan is risky. There is nothing worse than preparing for a particular sex of child, painting the nursery pink or blue and buying gender-stereotyped toys/clothing and finding your new baby is not the sex you were expecting. Even the results from an amniocentesis are not 100 percent accurate as samples are occasionally muddled up, although thankfully this is rare.

The usual way round the baby-of-unknown-sex dilemma is to choose neutral colours such as lavender, green, yellow and white (or a mix of both pink and blue) for clothes/nursery décor and to convince yourself that whatever sex arrives is all right as long as the baby is perfectly healthy.

Mothers and fathers/sons and daughters

For many people, having the ideal family means having one boy and one girl to 'replace' their parents in the scheme of life.

If you don't want to have children, then don't. However much you come to love them you will always wonder, 'What if? Where would my career be now if...?' It happened to my sister and I'm glad I made the personal decision not to have a baby. I must admit that as the menopause comes closer and closer I occasionally stop to reconsider, but my career and independence are everything to me ... I think my male employees are wary of me because I haven't shown the softness and femininity that automatically come from being a mother. Caroline

We had a boy first, then a girl, which is what I had always hoped for. I wasn't convinced it would happen, however, as I realized that every other woman in my family had always given birth to a girl first. Sarah

My relationship with my mother and my daughter are among the most important and loving and complex in my life. I have also an inspirational father and two glorious sons. Yet my relationships with them are complicated in a different way. Is it, quite simply, that my mother, my daughter and I are all female, a line of women, like Russian dolls who have emerged, the one from the other?

Extract from *Motherland*, Ann McFerran (Virago)

You may also find that the quality of your relationship with your child may differ depending on whether you have a son or a daughter: some women have always wanted a daughter to dress up and play with – echoes of their favourite doll from childhood – whereas others prefer the energy and mischievousness of boys.

My first baby was a boy. When I became pregnant again, I was certain I would have a little girl. I just knew, as I felt different in this pregnancy. When the baby was born and it was another boy, I couldn't believe it. I found it hard to love him at first and was angry with him – and myself – because he was the wrong sex. I soon became pregnant again, hoping to have my longed-for daughter. It was another boy, but this time I bonded with him immediately, and this also helped me learn to love my second son. Several years later, I became pregnant again. Because I now loved my three boys so dearly, I realized that the sex of the child no longer mattered. When I delivered our fourth son, we were just happy that he, like all the others, was healthy and perfect in his own way. Sally

When my son was born, my heart melted. My love for my son was as strong as that for my daughter and the love he gave in return seemed to double that which I gave. My daughter was very much a daddy's girl but my son and I grew to have such a strong love and bonding it surprised me. Circumstances required me to go back to work. It broke my heart to leave the children especially when my son would scream and cling to my coat. Many times I walked to work crying, unable to look back. Jane

While women often long for another female in the family, men often look forward to having at least one son to kick a football around with in the evenings and weekends. Some even joke about siring their own football team.

As a father-to-be I said all the right things: 'Oh I don't mind what we get as long as it's all right.' Secretly though, I longed for a boy. After an interminable labour on the hottest day of 1980 my wife gave birth to ... a girl ... and handed her to me. Putting a brave face on it, I took her in my arms. She looked me straight in the eye and gave me a look that said: 'From now on, mate, I'm going to run your life!' I instantly fell in love with her, and gave in without a struggle. This week she is 18 – she's still running my life (and I hope she always will). John

Gay parenting: Potential motherhood

by **Lisa Saffron**

In practical terms, having a baby changes your life in the same momentous ways for lesbians as for heterosexual women. But there are differences. Your relationship with your partner will change fundamentally and in ways not faced by heterosexual couples. If you are raising the child together, you will be working out what it means to both of you to be a mother and how important the biological connection is. Your relationship with your child's father will not affect your life if the donor is anonymous. But many lesbians choose to conceive using a known donor (see chapter 9). He may share the parenting with you, in which case your life will include the child's father to a large extent. Or he may have a more limited role, in which case you will be negotiating and refining that role throughout your child's life. Your relationship with your partner's children will change your life whether you are a step-parent to them or have been involved in their conception and birth.

Your life will also be affected by other people's attitudes towards lesbian mothers. You can't assume when you announce your pregnancy that your exciting news will be greeted with joy and that you, your partner and your children will be welcomed with open arms. Prejudice against homosexuality is widespread in society, its expression ranging from unintentional neglect to discrimination by privileging homosexuality, through to violent assault and outright gay-bashing. Your relationships with your parents and extended family, GP, midwives and other health workers, neighbours, colleagues at work, teachers at your children's school, friends and acquaintances will all be affected by their attitudes and by the way you confront prejudice.

Support is essential, both for your sake and for your children's. The best source of support is a strong community of lesbian mothers. There's no doubt that having a baby will change your life but the difficult changes can be coped with better if you are not alone.

What lesbian couples say ...

Kath is co-parenting their daughter, Ruth, with her partner, Judy, and says:

One of the most difficult things has been dealing with other women's (mainly lesbians') inability to get their heads and their words around the wholeness of our family. It makes me feel angry rather than anything else. It feels like I'm being dismissed. I do as much for Ruth as Judy does. I have as many sleepless nights. I have washed as many nappies. I take as much of the responsibility as Judy does. It makes me furious when people ask which one of us is her real/proper mother. The short reply is that we both are. Given that, I did have to recognize, sometimes painfully, from early on that Judy's biological relationship to Ruth was more significant than I had thought it might be. The months of breast-feeding were hard. I was jealous and felt I had to change and wash more nappies to compensate, had to wake up to fetch her for a feed in the night even if I couldn't deliver it. This became easier after the first few months when we moved on to mixed bottle/breast-feeding, which worked well for us despite the orthodoxy which says that bottle-feeding can distract babies from the breast.

Karen, 32, is in a lesbian relationship with partner Traci:

Both Traci and I are planning to get pregnant. It will be interesting to see how the issues about biological and non-biological mothers work out. To some extent, we expect that balance will be redressed when we have a second child. I want to go first as I'm slightly older and more neurotic about it. If I can't get pregnant and if Traci conceives at the drop of a hat, I will feel jealous and bitter, that I'd failed in some way. I'm sure there would be a whole gamut of rubbish to run through. These are things that a heterosexual couple doesn't have to deal with. However, Traci and I have worked through lots of things together and I guess we'd have to get round it some way. We're generally quite good at talking about things.

Jude is the lesbian mother of two daughters:

Both my pregnancy and my partner, Linda's pregnancy, enriched our relationship. The babies were very much wanted, planned and welcomed into our little family set-up. The sharing of each pregnancy, birth and baby was magic. Each time, it felt that someone special was joining us. It made us very happy. Neither of us felt put out at all by the arrival of either the first or second child perhaps because we had thought about it for a long time and had decided that we wanted to have children together. Lesbians are in a better position to worship their partner's pregnancy, especially if it's a child that they both want. I don't see how it could ever equal having a baby with a man since men can't experience growing a baby themselves.

Jean is in a lesbian relationship with partner Cathy:

I had Elaine when Cathy's daughter, Alice, was two and a half. It was absolute hell
with little moments of sublime joy that made it all worthwhile. Alice felt displaced. I
breast-fed Elaine for a long time so that Cathy felt excluded from a relationship
with Elaine. I know that I did really want this intense relationship with my baby but
I wasn't very honest about what I was doing. I didn't feel that I should or could
have it. It was quite destructive. I don't think we thought about roles. The roles are
quite clear when there's only one. Cathy was Alice's biological mother and was very
generous with Alice in a way that I wasn't with Elaine. I fed Alice. I was very
involved with her as a baby but when Elaine came along and Alice was still very
demanding, the family split down the middle and stayed like that for quite a long
time. We were all exhausted. I feel very different about my own child, Elaine, than I
do about Cathy's daughter, Alice. My relationship with Alice is much clearer.
Having your own child opens up a whole can of worms. The relationship between
the mother and the daughter is immensely intense. I made it intense and I loved
that intensity to start with but of course it doesn't go away. It's not like a
relationship that you can end.

Liz is in a lesbian relationship with partner Carol:

When my partner and I started to seriously consider having a baby, we had to face
the fact that, as lesbians, we would be minority parents. How would we deal with
any prejudice we came across and, more importantly, how would we help our child
cope with the outside world's attitudes to them growing up in a gay household?

In the event, things have gone far better than, I think, either of us hoped. Our son
is now three and, although we occasionally see or hear a rant in the media against
gay parents, we have not come up against any overt prejudice in our daily lives.

Being pregnant was almost like becoming public property. Suddenly I was under
scrutiny from a range of strangers who were to become intimate with my lifestyle.
At first this was difficult because I was never sure of the reaction I would get. But
the medical profession generally didn't seem that bothered and the midwives at
the hospital where our son was born didn't turn a hair. Carol was treated as my
partner and received both respect and consideration.

Our health visitor has been brilliant, making it clear that, as far as she is
concerned, our son is fortunate to have two parents who clearly dote on him.

In the rosy afterglow of birth and the subsequent frenetic weeks getting to know
our son, we lost sight of the fact that we were not regarded by officialdom as a
'real' family. We were reminded of this fact, harshly, when we went to register the

birth. Having admitted that I was not married, the registrar then addressed every question to me and only my name went on the birth certificate. Carol was left on the sidelines. She had no legal status and no recognition of her involvement. It put a damper on the event.

But, on a much more positive note, we have been able to do something about this. We have obtained a residency order from the High Court which gives Carol parental responsibility for our son until he is 16 years old. We are now a recognized family unit.

Closer to home, what about our families? Well, it certainly took some of our relatives a while to get used to the idea. Not least, because Carol's brother, also gay, was the donor. There were a few odd utterances such as 'The child will be psychologically damaged' but people came round in the end. The support we have received from our families has been very important to us.

But, in many ways, the people who can make or break a situation are neighbours, friends and the people you meet every day. And here we have also been fortunate. We are honest about our situation and have been rewarded with tolerance.

At some point our son is going to realize that other children have a dad and ask about his. We intend to be totally honest with him about his origins and, as his donor is also his 'uncle', they will already know each other. But we also recognise that he will have to learn discretion about who he tells. He may not even want anyone to know and we would have to cope with going back into the closet in some circumstances.

Chapter 3:
Potential Fatherhood

Once upon a time, men were reluctant to admit that they might like to have a baby one day. The need to be a father did not fit the stereotyped macho image of the he-man. Wanting children was the province of women and, if anything, men lived in fear of their girlfriends becoming pregnant and trapping them into marriage. As contraception became more sophisticated, women increasingly put their career commitments first, postponing childbirth until their biological clock threatened to run out. Men don't have a biological clock when it comes to procreation and, assuming they do not develop erectile dysfunction, can continue to father children into their 70s and beyond, especially with the advent of drugs such as Viagra. Even if impotence does strike, many medical treatments are available to help regain potency and fertility.

Reports of falling sperm counts and reduced male fertility are starting to make more and more men think about having a baby. The owner of one dating agency estimates that nine out of ten men in their 30s are actively seeking a partner because they wish to start a family. Some say a baby is the new fashion accessory for the sexy, sensitive man. Others claim it is all to do with the new millennium – a need to mark the beginning of a new century with a lasting memento. And there is little so lasting as the relationship between parent and child.

Wanting to be a father

There are many reasons why a man may want to have a baby one day, including a deep-seated, biological urge to reproduce. The longing to have a baby is not just a female experience – men can experience a deep desire for children, too.

I'd done everything else I wanted to do, and started to think what next? Having a baby seemed the next logical step in life. That's how I justified it to everyone else, anyway. In reality, I was feeling incredibly broody – much more so than my wife, who didn't seem that bothered whether we had kids or not, really. Neville

My own dad was quite elderly when I came along. I wanted to have my own children while I was still young enough to kick a football around with them, build sandcastles and fly a kite in the park. John

I can remember the swell of pride when I cuddled my sister's first child and being told I'd make a great dad – a natural. I wanted to go right out and have one myself. So I did. David

I was first aware of feeling broody in my late 20s. But I didn't want a baby at any cost. It had to be with the right person. Sean

Increasing numbers of men are finding their desire to become a dad thwarted by the career aspirations of their partners, as women increasingly decide to postpone motherhood rather than put their careers on hold.

My friends all have children and are always asking me when I'm going to settle down and have a family. It never used to bother me. Now it does, as most women I've gone out with in the last few years don't seem to want babies – not until their career is sorted, anyway. Paul

And once in a stable relationship, it is usually the female rather than the male who decides when the time is right to become parents.

My wife decided when we should have our first baby. I imagine it's the same with many couples. We had talked about it of course – the changes it would bring, the costs, her career. We eventually made the decision, and she stopped taking the Pill. But the precise moment, that was hers. I could still see one more holiday, or perhaps a new car ... It happened when she felt right, and was really wanting to. We were working abroad at the time. The nausea we put down to strange foods. Even the missed period could have been the effects of travel. But when the penny finally dropped, it did everything I expected it to. It totally changed our lives, and immediately became the most important thing in them. Paul

I realize that having a baby is a big decision for a woman as she is the one that has to carry the baby for nine months and therefore decides when the time is right. But I feel almost envious that she can experience a child growing inside her tummy. I'd love to experience that, too. Dave

The impact of a baby will be different in each relationship. The traditional dad who goes out to work long hours and rarely changes nappies or gets up to feed a crying baby at night, may notice little difference to his lifestyle except that of another drain on his wallet. The modern father who is prepared to share the baby care and bathes, dresses, changes and feeds his baby, however, will find his lifestyle changed for ever.

All the things I had worried about certainly happened. We got poorer, lives revolved around our baby, and our social lives vanished

overnight. But the wonderful part of it was that it didn't matter. No, more than that, we welcomed it. The next promotion, the endless running around 'achieving' things, suddenly seemed less important. Surely, having children is, for most of us, the most important thing we ever do. Yes, they are everything you ever feared, but after 20 years now, life would have been so sterile, so empty, without them.
Paul

Being a father will certainly affect your social life – a new baby is very tying and can also be very tiring. You may find that lack of sleep means you don't feel like going out even when you have the opportunity.

Not wanting to be a father

Even though it has become increasingly trendy to upgrade from lad to dad, many men are far from ready to father a baby. They may have many reasons for feeling like this this, ranging from a fear of commitment or not having found the right partner, to still having a bucket full of wild oats to sow.

If you feel you don't want a baby yet, but your partner does, you will need to talk things through very carefully. If you give in and agree, or suddenly find your partner pregnant by 'accident', you may start to feel trapped, angry or even used. If you feel ambivalent about being a father, say so. It is important that each partner in a relationship knows how the other feels.

Not agreeing to father a child when requested to do so may endanger your relationship, however. According to a Gallup Survey on behalf of First Response (a pregnancy test brand), one in five women questioned who were in a relationship said they would walk out on their partner if he refused to let them have a baby. Another one in five said they would seriously consider leaving. This is an issue that needs to be fully resolved between both partners before throwing the contraceptives away.

Attending the birth

Just a generation ago, it was unusual for men to attend the birth of their child. They were relegated to a waiting room, caricatured by pale faces, messy hair with much pacing up and down – the imagined horrors in the delivery room fuelled by the grunts, groans and screams that escaped through the door.

My wife was exhausted after having the baby and also suffered mild postnatal depression. I took a month off work to look after them both – I didn't have bags under my eyes, I had suitcases! I never realized what hard work such a little thing can be. It was almost a relief to get back to the pressures of the office. Simon

When my mates heard I was going to be a father, I was described as having 'succumbed'. While they were happy to wet the baby's head, I haven't seen a lot of them since, and we seem to have little in common any more. And, like me, any new acquaintances I meet who have children seem to have little time for socializing. Sad, really. Greg

Seeing my children born brought me closer to them and their mother – it was eye-opening to see what she was prepared to go through to have my babies. The excitement of seeing the first lock of hair in the birth canal was better than seeing England win the World Cup. Being there for my wife was also important – rubbing her back, helping her breathe through contractions, holding her foot while she pushed – even giving her someone to scream at – made me feel actively involved in the delivery. Philip

Nowadays, the father's presence at the birth of his babies is virtually universal in Western cultures. Men also tend to accompany their pregnant partner to antenatal classes, parentcraft sessions and breast-feeding workshops. It is important for men to read as much as possible about childbirth beforehand – and to realize that it is quite normal for it to be a messy, bloody business.

My wife gave birth by Caesarean at the hospital in which she also worked as a doctor. They had had several unfortunate experiences with staff deliveries and therefore left nothing to chance. By the time two consultant anaesthetists, two consultant obstetricians, and two consultant paediatricians filled the room, there was little space left for me. I saw very little of my son being born – there were too many bodies around the operating table. I was the first person our son saw when he opened his eyes however – a moment I will treasure for ever. Richard

Although some men seem to feel their input to the baby ends after the moment of conception, wanting to be a father means being prepared to support your pregnant partner throughout pregnancy, usually labour – if you jointly agree that is what you both want – and beyond. Talk to friends and relatives about their experiences of becoming a father and try to formulate your own ideals of the kind of father, co-parent and partner you want to be.

Your partner's pregnancy and your sex life

Having a baby will undoubtedly affect your sex life, and this is something you need to be prepared for when you are both thinking of having a baby. A woman's sex drive can go up, go down or remain the same during pregnancy – every woman, and every pregnancy is different. Emotional influences play a big role, especially the duality of being both a sexually active person and a mother or mother-to-be. Often a woman's sex drive goes up in the middle three months of pregnancy due to hormone changes and increased blood flow to the genitals which increase vaginal lubrication and make orgasm easier to achieve and more intense. Sex drive may be low during the first three months – due to tiredness and morning sickness – and again during the last three months of pregnancy, when tiredness and increasing size drives sex lower down the agenda. It is important to realize that low sex drive is perfectly normal at the end of pregnancy.

This is because levels of the milk-producing hormone, prolactin, start to rise and prolactin has a profound damping effect on a woman's sex drive. Loss of sex drive is not necessarily inevitable at the end of pregnancy however, as high levels of oestrogen and progesterone help to neutralize the prolactin effects. Low sex drive is almost inevitable immediately after having the baby, however, and affects at least four out of every five women (see below). Not surprisingly, this can place a great strain on a relationship. Once the man understands it is a normal hormone response and that his wife has not stopped loving him because of the baby, it is just a question of time before everything comes right again.

 There are also occasions when sex should be avoided during pregnancy, most usually when there is a risk of miscarriage or preterm labour. If this is the case, always follow the instructions of your partner's midwife or doctors.

Interestingly, fathers-to-be often find their own sex drive goes down during their partner's pregnancy. This may relate to fear of harming the baby, finding the pregnant female shape less appealing, or possibly as a result of changes in female pheromones – odourless chemicals we all secrete which affect the behaviour of others – that make you feel more protective rather than sexual towards her.

Prospective fathers may worry about the imminent birth and what their partner has to go through, or have subconscious conflicting feelings about their partner's dual role as a mother and lover. These feelings are very common and nothing to worry about. Things will eventually get back to normal, but it may take several months from when the baby is born. An unfortunate statistic in a late 1980s survey claimed that 40 percent of men were sexually unfaithful during their partner's pregnancy. The damage their relationship would sustain if they were found out surely means it is never worth it.

> I don't like to admit it, but I just don't find my wife's eight-months pregnant body sexy. Will I ever fancy her again? Nate

> I was unfaithful to my wife when she was six months pregnant. I hadn't planned it, it just happened and I instantly regretted it. Unfortunately I caught genital warts, which I guess serves me right. They went with treatment, but I live in fear of my wife catching them and finding out – especially as they're linked with an increased risk of cervical cancer. My message to any man contemplating being unfaithful to his wife is – don't do it, mate. Think what you've got to lose. D

I used to worry that the baby could see or hear us having sex and this put me off towards the end of pregnancy. I never found out if this was true or not – I didn't like to ask! Jason

The developing baby cannot see you making love, but he will certainly hear you. From around 20 weeks of development, a baby starts to become aware of sounds outside the womb and will soon learn to recognize his mother's and father's voices, along with any others he hears regularly. When you make love, your baby will be aware that something is happening and it may wake him if he is sleeping, but he will not understand what is going on.

Your sex life after the baby is born

Many men assume their partners' sex drive will quickly return to normal after having a baby. This is not usually the case, however, especially in women who continue to breast-feed. High levels of the prolactin hormone diminish libido and often make the female sex drive disappear altogether. This is one of nature's ways of helping to ensure a new mother does not become pregnant again while her baby is still highly dependent on her. Eight out of ten new mothers therefore experience a loss of sex drive – but few couples are warned of this effect. It is perfectly natural and does not mean your partner does not fancy you any more, or that the baby has taken your place in her affections. This effect is only temporary. After childbirth, prolactin levels return to normal (to non-pregnant levels within eight days if breast-feeding does not occur). They rise again during breast-feeding to help stimulate a continued supply of milk, then start to fall after around three months, so that milk production continues with normal prolactin levels. There is therefore no need to stop your partner breast-feeding just to retrieve her libido – breast-feeding is by far the healthiest option for the baby (unless the mother is HIV positive). All that's required is a little patience; in one survey, a quarter of women interviewed a year after giving birth said they enjoyed sex more then than they did before conceiving.

Other factors that will affect your partner's sex drive immediately after having the baby are soreness – especially if she has had stitches – fearing that she is too big (either vaginally or overweight) to please you, low self-esteem, anxiety about coping with the baby, fear of further pregnancy and postnatal depression. It is important not to take her disinterest in sex personally – make sure you discuss your feelings openly so each of you knows how the other feels. Even if she has gone off sex temporarily you need to continue showing affection to each other while working through this time.

You may also appreciate being forewarned that if your partner is breast-feeding she may start to leak milk when you make love. This is because the hormone that stimulates release of milk, oxytocin, is also secreted during orgasm and when the nipples are stimulated. Leaking of milk usually only occurs during breast-feeding when milk production is established. It may occur during late pregnancy in some women, however, especially those who have previously breast-fed, but this is uncommon.

Being a working father

One of the key findings of a report commissioned on behalf of the Department for Education and Employment in Great Britain in 1996 was that, although children are growing up in more affluent surroundings as a result of their parents working, they are also spending less and less time with their parents. The report found that 85 percent of fathers were employed in 1994, compared with 70 percent of other men, 59 percent of mothers and 70 percent of other women. Unfortunately, fathers were also more likely to be working longer hours than non-fathers. In 1994, 57 percent of fathers were working more than 40 hours a week, compared with 39 percent of other men.

A Gallup survey on behalf of First Response found that 76 percent of those questioned believed that new fathers should have the legal right to paternity leave, with most favouring between four days and one month at home. Nine percent of men in the Midlands and Wales felt men should get more than a three-month paternity leave, compared with 16 percent of men in the south and 17 percent in the north and Scotland.

Another extensive survey undertaken on behalf of the Department for Education and Employment interviewed 1,311 representative employers and 2,051 new mothers (and their partners) who had had a baby in June 1996. The survey looked at the provisions of the following four family-friendly work practices (see chapter 4):

- extra statutory maternity benefits over and above the minimum requirements set by law
- availability of paternity leave

My wife totally went off sex for six months after having the baby. She joked she never wanted to see another penis again. I tried to understand, but the continual rejection was very hurtful. Especially as she seemed to have more time for the baby than me. Ross

- employer contributions towards the cost of childcare
- flexible working options.

The survey showed that overall, a father's entitlement to family-friendly working practices are more limited than for women although this depended on their position and chosen career. Twenty-three percent of those in professional positions were able to take advantage of some form of work flexibility, compared with only 5 percent of craft workers and 3 percent of manual workers.

Only one in four employers offered paternity leave for new fathers, although most new fathers did take time off – an average of eight days – by using up paid holiday entitlements (47 percent) or a combination of holiday and paternity leave (25 percent). Of those who received paid paternity leave (around 40 percent) this only averaged four days. One in six fathers said they were able to work from home around the time of their child's birth.

Men were less likely than women to have access to planned career breaks on becoming a new father, with only 15 percent of men (compared with 33 percent of women) saying this option was available for some employees at their place of work. Men are also less likely to be offered a non-standard working week (e.g. spreading full-time work over four rather than five days) or to have access to switching from full-time to part-time work, either temporarily or permanently to help care for their new family. Of those men who said their employer operated a part-time working scheme (29 percent), only 8 percent said they were entitled to it, and only 2 percent took advantage of it.

Research suggests that fathers are beginning to suffer from the strain of juggling work and family life. Work pressures also mean it is difficult to meet commitments and responsibilities at home. Many feel they are missing out on their children growing up and regret the sacrifices made to family life because of their careers.

More and more fathers are becoming aware of what they are missing at home. Those that work may leave home before junior is awake, and arrive back again after the baby is asleep in bed. Many feel they hardly know their children and are often cast as the villain of the piece who is expected to chastise the kids when Mum has had-it-up-to-here all week.

As a result, more and more men are thinking of taking up flexible work time options (see chapter 4) to achieve greater quality of life and to spend more time with their children. Some parents manage to share childcare by both partners working part-time, and dovetailing their hours. In other cases men take extended paternity or special leave when their baby is born or accept voluntarily reduced hours, or term-time working (see chapter 4).

New Ways to Work, an organisation formed to help those who want to combine parenting and a career (see Resources, page 244), feel that balance between work and family are issues for men as well as women and include 'flexible men' as role models in each of their newsletters to help encourage men to take up flexible options. They also sell a comprehensive pack called *Balanced Lives: Changing Work Patterns for Men* which draws from the experiences of 100 men working reduced and flexible hours, taking career breaks or who have chosen to work from home in a variety of roles.

Being a house-husband

Fathers now play a more active role in parenting than was the norm just a generation ago. Modern fathers are willing – and expected – to change nappies, help with feeds, bathing and getting up at night and to see to the needs of their new offspring in general. In some cases, it will make sense for fathers to stay at home while their partner continues to work once the baby is born. Another option is for fathers to work part-time or more flexible hours, so they have more time to spend with their child as he or she grows up (for more information, see chapters 4 and 5).

> Having a baby and being a house-husband have made me more appreciative of the difficulties mothers have running a household and looking after a new-born. I now need less sleep, get less sleep and ignore the bags under my eyes when I look in the mirror in the morning. I am now more forgetful than before. Richard

I'd seriously consider giving up my job to look after a baby if my partner earned enough. Adrian

I consciously decided to go into teaching so I would have lots of time to spend with my children during holidays. I will also see quite a bit of them in school once they are old enough. Rob

I took three months off when my daughter was born. Looking back, the time we spent together was so precious. Allan

Not for lunch
by **Simon Brett**

I don't know who was the first wife to say 'I took you for better, for worse, but not for lunch', when her husband announced that he was about to start working from home, but now those words have gone into folk memory.

Making your house your office is not, however, all negative – particularly when there are small children around. I've been working from home for nearly twenty years, and one of the great bonuses of that experience has been being around to watch my children grow up.

The typical masculine career is still totally back-to-front, so far as childcare is concerned. A man in his late twenties or early thirties – the stage he and his wife are likely to start breeding – is usually at the most pressured time of his working life. That is when he is going to 'make it' or not. That is when a boss will want him to prove his keenness by working long hours and volunteering for extra duties. That's when he's likely to be travelling most. Just when his children are small and developing quickest, their father will be at home for the shortest amount of time.

And, when he's got high up enough the career structure to take things a little easier, in many cases his children will be grown up and gone.

There are plenty of absent fathers who've abandoned wives and children, but even the most tightly knit family units can still suffer from Absentee Father Syndrome.

In the average male working life, contact with small children is frequently reduced to hasty farewells in the morning, when father and offspring are grumpy and half-awake, and brief kisses goodnight when both are scratchy and fractious after a tiring day (and even that is only when the father makes a point of coming home from work particularly early).

Weekends are not a lot better. The father is short-tempered, twitchily withdrawing from his work anxieties on Saturday morning, and after lunch on Sunday starting to twitch again about the week ahead. It's no way to build bonding relationships between parents and children.

Women are famously guilty about juggling the demands of work and family, but men can suffer just as badly. They're missing something and they know it. No amount of calls from the office can make up for the hugs, games and stories that should have happened. In the worst case of Absentee Father Syndrome I've heard of, a small boy thought the telephone was called a 'Daddy' because that was his only means of communication with his father.

Only my eldest child can recall my going out to work, and I regret those few years when I wasn't around, watching her develop all the time. With the other two I was a fixture, another bit of furniture that was always there. When my second child started school and had friends home, my study door would open and little faces peer round to see this strange phenomenon of 'the daddy who worked at home'.

The drawbacks were very few. True, it was a bit of a shock when I first gave up going out to work. I was used to the forty-minute journey from the office as a time to change personality from my work self to my home self. On my first day of writing at home, as I emerged from my study at six o'clock, my wife immediately shoved two squalling brats into my arms. No time to change personality there. But I soon adjusted.

The other big drawback was Empty Nest Syndrome. Fathers who work at home suffer from this just as much as mothers. Each advance your child makes that takes him or her away from the house for longer leaves you with a little pang. I can still remember the desolation I felt when my youngest child started going to school in the afternoons. Up until then, all through his life, I'd taken him for a walk by the river straight after lunch. Suddenly I was left having to make my own entertainment.

And the house still feels empty when they all go back to school or university. Working from home, I'm afraid, does encourage any natural tendencies one might have towards being a sentimental old fool.

But the benefits far outweigh any of these disadvantages. Practical benefits, as well as emotional ones. With me working at home, when one of the babies was having a sleep, my wife could go out to shop or have coffee with a friend, secure in the knowledge that there was someone there in the event of a disaster or just early waking.

Yes, I recommend it. It's enriched my life enormously – and I hope it's enriched my children's. They certainly seem as delightful to me as they did when they were born. I think we all know each other well – and I don't think any of us has any illusions about any of the others.

Governments keep talking about giving more paternity leave. The odd extra week or month would certainly help. But it's not enough. I feel sorry for fathers who haven't been around the house for all the years that their children were growing up.

Simon Brett is the author of (among 50 other books) the bestselling *How To Be A Little Sod, Little Sod's Next Step* and *Not Another Little Sod!,* which chronicle a baby's first three years, seen from the baby's point of view.

Gay parenting: Potential fatherhood
by **Lisa Saffron**

Most gay fathers are fathers who were once married or lived with a woman. Some gay fathers remain married because they feel there is no alternative, fearing they would be denied contact with their children if they were open about their sexuality. The majority do not remain in a heterosexual relationship once they accept their sexual identity, but when a gay man leaves, the mother is more likely to be awarded custody.

It is more common for lesbian mothers to be living with their children than for gay fathers. The latter may find it more difficult to tell their children they are gay than do lesbian mothers. In most cases the children react with understanding and acceptance but researchers have found that gay fathers get more negative reactions than lesbian mothers. It is also harder for gay fathers to integrate their parenting identity and their sexual identity than it is for lesbian mothers.

Surrogacy is one way for a gay man to become both a biological and a social father. This involves an agreement with a woman to conceive by donor insemination, carry the baby to term, and give birth but not to function as a social mother. Commercial surrogacy is illegal in Britain and though it is possible to make informal arrangements, it is not often done. In many parts of the United States, commercial surrogacy is legal and gay men have become fathers this way as well as through informal arrangements, sometimes with lesbians acting as the surrogate. Gay men may also become fathers through donor insemination, adoption and fostering.

Donor insemination is a relatively simple process by which a man donates his sperm. When done at a clinic, the donor is always anonymous but lesbians often make informal arrangements with men for 'self-insemination'. In these situations, the social relationship between the donor and the child is negotiated in advance between the mother or mothers-to-be and the donor. Children sometimes redefine these relationships as they become older. Where the donor's identity is known, children can initiate contact if they choose.

Some donors arrange to be co-parents and they are fathers in both the biological and social sense of the word. Many lesbians prefer the donor to remain anonymous and not become a father. Other lesbian mothers want the child to know the donor's identity but to have no contact. Some want the donor to have some kind of contact with the child but not a parental relationship.

If you are asked to be a donor, think about it seriously before you agree and do not go ahead if you feel uneasy. You need to consider how you might feel knowing that you had fathered a child or if you were contacted one day by the child. Some very young children ask to see their donors and the mothers may want to arrange this. Or the child might be a teenager or young adult before deciding to trace you. How would you feel about this? You are being asked to donate your sperm to a woman who will be raising the child without a man as father, either on her own or with a lesbian partner. You are doing this on the understanding that you will not insist on parental responsibility for the child that results. You will not be asked to act as a father or pay any maintenance or have any parental obligations towards the child. You may be asked if you are willing to be contacted by the child if the child wants to meet its genetic father.

What gay men say ...

Dileep donated sperm to more than 12 lesbian couples:

I haven't met any of the children. Women I'm a donor for now, are frequently friends of women I've been a donor for in the past, so I get passed on little bits of information about the existing children. Recently the first couple I was a donor for back in 1986 asked me to come over to talk about being a donor for the second partner in the relationship who also wanted to have a child. I visited their home and talked this through and I saw photos of their child who was then four. Although I didn't meet the child, it certainly gave me a buzz to see the photo. It was really nice to know the child's name but I don't feel I have the right to meet that child or any of the others I've been a donor for. The child has a right to ask to see me. I've always seen it operating that way around. All of the mothers have my consent to pass on information about me to their children if they choose to. A few have indicated now that they do want to pass on the information. The majority say they don't. I think their decisions on that may change in the future.

Alex, a gay man who is donating sperm to a lesbian friend, Sandra, says:

When I was asked if I would be interested in donating sperm, I said I was open to the idea. I was particularly interested because I know that lesbians are having increasing difficulties getting access to sperm banks. For me, donating sperm is something of a gesture of support to the lesbian community, an opportunity to bridge gaps. There are so many divides between the lesbian and gay male communities. I don't want to be a parent and I don't want any involvement with the child. My life doesn't allow for me to take on that responsibility – financially and everything else. I have enough problems looking after myself. I don't think there is any chance I would change. Sandra and I decided that if we become closer friends, then my involvement with the child will be because of my friendship with her rather than just because of being the biological father. If Sandra decides she doesn't want a father around at all, that's fine. I accept that and if she decides that she wants to be open about it, then I accept that she wants to be open about it.

Rick has a seven-year-old son, David:

I came out just after my marriage had ended, when my son was 18 months old. When I did eventually have the courage, there were still unanswered questions but I was clear that I was not going to lose contact with my son and that I, as a gay father, was going to bring him up. I have a regular pattern of contact established, which means I can be involved in my son's school, with some of the day-to-day aspects of being a parent and with some of the 'extras', like days out. It never seems like enough time and I always find the house suddenly too quiet when he's at his mum's, but as a compromise between getting the balance right for him and for the two of us as parents, it more or less works. Because David was only 18 months old when we separated, I was able to bring him up knowing that I was gay. Alongside everything else we did, he had gay children's stories, came to Gay Pride (the annual gay rights event) and Stonewall (the gay rights group), knew other children with lesbian or gay parents and met my boyfriends. This was not something that his mother agreed with and he also heard a lot of homophobic comments from her. Although I have found a lot of the issues over the past five years difficult to resolve, they have not been as difficult as I expected them to be when I was still married and was just imagining them.

Mary, the 19-year-old daughter of a gay man, says:

My parents split up when I was two and a half which means I have no memory of them in a relationship together. My mum died when I was five, but even before that, it was always just me and my dad. All the time I was growing up, the fact that my dad was gay was a normal part of my life. It wasn't a big deal for me. My mum's death is the most traumatic thing that's ever happened to me in my life. It overshadows any problems I might have had about my dad's homosexuality. When I was growing up, my dad identified himself more as a single parent than as a gay father. He was worried about coming out, and had a generalized anxiety that I would be taken away if someone official discovered he was gay. I don't know if my dad told me to keep quiet about it or if I just picked the message up. My dad's been more active in the gay community since he's been with his current boyfriend, Mark. He and Mark go out to clubs a lot more than he did with the boyfriends he had when I was younger. Then it was hard to get a baby-sitter and he didn't go out as much. On the whole, it's a straight world with heterosexuality pushed on you from every direction. Like everyone else, I've been influenced by that. But because my dad's gay, I've also had the added benefit of a positive experience of homosexuality. As a result, I feel comfortable with gay men. He and I can talk about men in a slightly more equal way and I think he understands me more than a straight man would. People need to hear that it's perfectly acceptable for gay men to be parents and that it doesn't make any difference to the child. What's important is how much the child is loved and how well the parents look after their child. There are so many parents out there that are not doing a decent job of bringing up their children while my dad without exception has done a good job for me. I am really proud of him for being what he is.

Chapter 4:
Looking Ahead: To work or not to work?

According to a 1998 survey of 5,500 men and women interviewed by the consultancy firm WFD and business magazine *Management Today*, half of those questioned said they regretted sacrificing family life for the sake of their careers. Two out of three mothers felt they had less time for their personal lives as a result of juggling the needs of work and home, while half felt that pressure at work left them barely able to meet all their responsibilities and commitments at home. Many felt they had missed seeing their children grow up and, although four out of five people questioned said that home should always come first, only two out of five felt they had got the balance right. One in ten women said they had delayed having children or sacrificed their chance to become a mother for their careers.

When thinking about having a baby, you need to think long and hard about how and when this will dovetail with your work plans. You will need to consider whether or not you wish to continue working during the pregnancy, and if so at what stage you take maternity leave. You also need to consider whether or not you want to return to work once the baby is born. Don't feel guilty if you do decide to go back to work. Even though the above survey showed that women are struggling to balance work and home, more mothers than fathers said they gained most of their satisfaction in life from pursuing a career. Work also provides a safety valve from the stress that can occur in domestic life – one in three employees said there were times they would rather escape to work than cope with a dependent parent or crying child at home.

Maternity leave

If you think you want to have a baby one day, it is worth reading your

My company had a good maternity package – I was entitled to six weeks maternity leave on 9/10 salary, then 32 weeks at half salary provided I indicated my intention to return. Jane

I had planned to work right up until the 38th week of pregnancy – I wasn't going to let a little thing like pregnancy stop me! In the end, this became impractical. I couldn't physically sit at my desk as my bump got in the way. By 34 weeks, my blood pressure started creeping up and my GP signed me off sick which meant my maternity leave kicked in automatically at work. In retrospect, I was more than ready to stop work by 30 weeks. I hadn't realized just how clumsy and exhausted I was going to feel, even though I was off my feet for most of the day. Gail

Staff Handbook (if you have one), Contract of Employment or the Maternity Information Pack provided by your employer to see what maternity leave you are entitled to, and the policy regarding return to work. Don't be afraid to raise the issue with your employer as you have a variety of legal rights when you are pregnant and work. The company you work for may well be thinking of introducing more flexibility into the workplace. There is also up-to-date information on your entitlement to statutory maternity leave in chapter 7, and from the Maternity Alliance (see Resources page 235). If you are self-employed, you are entitled to Maternity Allowance in a maximum of 18 weeks, which is designed for women who are not currently employed, but have paid standard rate NI contributions for at least 26 of the 66 weeks before their baby is due. Contact your local Social Security office for claim form MA1.

Many pregnant women decide to keep working for as long as possible during pregnancy so that they can enjoy the majority of their maternity leave at home with their baby after the birth. This is not a good idea. Aim to stop working by around the 30-32nd week of your pregnancy if possible. After this time increased rest and relaxation are vitally important for both your own health and that of your growing baby. Prolonged standing, for example, is linked with an increased risk of preterm delivery and having a low birth weight baby. From the 30th week of pregnancy, it becomes increasingly important to lie down on your side, or sit with your feet up, for at least an hour mid-morning and mid-afternoon as this increases blood circulation through the placenta and carries oxygen and nutrients to your baby. Work stress can also have a harmful effect on your developing baby, who may become over-sensitive to the effects of stress hormones. Some research suggests that babies born to mothers who were excessively stressed or anxious during pregnancy, or who did more than eight hours' physical work in the last three months, are at as great a risk of low birth weight, small head size, impaired neurological development and preterm delivery as babies born to mothers who smoked cigarettes throughout their pregnancy. Some research also suggests that stress during pregnancy may increase the risk of your baby becoming anxious or depressed in later life. If you do work towards the end of pregnancy, try to keep regular hours and to avoid working night shifts.

Employers are usually flexible and will change your work obligations so you can sit down for most of the day as your pregnancy progresses (regulations require employers to provide a suitable place to rest for women who are pregnant or breast-feeding – see chapter 7 for more information).

Safety at work

When you eventually become pregnant, your employer has an obligation under the Health and Safety at Work regulations to ensure you are not exposed to potentially harmful industrial chemicals, gases or radiation. Employers have a specific duty to take particular account of risks to new and expectant mothers in the workplace. A new mother is defined as someone who has given birth within the previous six months (including stillbirth occurring after 24 weeks of pregnancy), or who is breast-feeding.

Some risks are especially hazardous at the very beginning of pregnancy (working with radiation exposure or chemicals, for example), or even before you are certain you are pregnant, in which case your employer should tell you about potential risks if you could, in the future, become pregnant. It is therefore important to consider these risks before planning to have a baby.

If there is a significant risk at work to either your own health or that of your baby, your employer will need to make changes to your work conditions or hours, or offer suitable alternative work. This is particularly relevant for any woman working night shifts, although there is no evidence at present of any particular risks to pregnant or breast-feeding women from working at night by itself. Having to work shifts may put you off thinking about getting pregnant, but it is useful to know that if you do decide to become pregnant and your doctor agrees that working nights does cause problems for your pregnancy, you can provide your employer with a medical certificate stating this fact. Your employer must then consider offering you suitable alternative daytime work (on terms and conditions that are as favourable as your current ones) if any is available. If it is not possible to change your work hours or conditions to avoid any possible work-related risks, then you are entitled to paid leave for as long as necessary to protect your own and your baby's health and safety. This obligation comes into force once you have informed your employer in writing that you are pregnant.

If you are planning to have a baby and are exposed to any of the following potentially harmful agents or work conditions, seek further

I worked in a noisy factory, and realized it was time to give up when my baby started jumping as if startled every time something clanged. Tina advice from your employer of the Health and Safety Executive (see Resources, page 244):

- shocks, vibration or movement (e.g. riding in off-road vehicles)
- heavy lifting where there is a risk of injury
- prolonged exposure to loud noise
- ionizing radiation
- extremes of heat or cold
- prolonged standing
- exposure to nauseating smells
- excessive physical or mental pressure
- working at heights, underground, in confined spaces or on slippery surfaces
- working in compressed air (e.g. diving)
- having to wear restrictive protective clothing
- biological agents classified as hazard groups 2, 3 or 4 by the Advisory Committee on Dangerous Pathogens
- chemical substances labelled R40, R45, R46, R47, R61, R63 or R64
- mercury
- lead
- cytotoxic drugs
- pesticides
- carbon monoxide.

There is no evidence that using a computer terminal, or sitting in front of a VDU screen is harmful to you or your baby during pregnancy, however, as long as you follow good ergonomic practice:

- ensure your chair, desk and screen are ergonomically adjusted for you
- have good back support from an adjustable chair
- use a wrist rest
- use a foot rest
- use a paper holder
- sit up straight and avoid crossing your legs or ankles
- take a regular screen break every 15 minutes by getting up, walking around and stretching your arms and legs.

The work dilemma

Deciding whether or not to go back to work after having your baby is rarely simple or straightforward. Just as nothing can prepare you for how you will feel when you first hold your baby in your arms, nothing can prepare you for the dilemma about whether or not to return to work, and it is worth thinking about this well in advance. Be prepared to change your mind, however. A Gallup survey on behalf of First Response pregnancy test kit found that out of 43 percent of new or expectant mums who had planned to return to work after the baby was born, 80 percent carried their plans through and 20 percent decided not to once the baby had arrived. Interestingly, 90 percent of those questioned who returned to work did so to hold a managerial or professional position.

You may not have to face the decision immediately as you may already have opted for the role of housewife and have previously left paid employment, or your partner may stay at home instead of you. Alternatively, you may have had the decision taken out of your hands through unemployment and lack of suitable local job options. If you are employed though, you will need to think in advance about how having a baby will affect your future career.

The basic options available for new parents who work vary from job to job, but any of the following is a possibility:

- You may decide to give up paid work altogether and stay at home.

- Taking unpaid leave (e.g. a career break, sabbatical or extended maternity leave) with the option to return after a certain period of time may be a viable option.

- You may be able to return to work part-time either with set hours, flexible hours, voluntarily reduced working hours (usually with full-time hours voluntarily reduced from 5 percent to 50 percent), annual hours (in which you agree a work pattern and number of hours to be worked over a 12-month period), term-time working or a job share (where two people share one full-time job between them).

- It may be workable for you to return to work full-time with set or flexible hours.

- Working from home for your employer (remote or home-based work, of which one type, teleworking, requires up-to-date information technology) may be workable.

The other main option is self-employment, which can either entail controlling your own work hours away from home, or working completely from home.

Should you stay at home?

Some new mothers strongly believe that, having had a baby, it is their duty to stay at home. Others simply want to be there to meet the needs of their family, share their growing up and provide the love and close attention young children need.

> Bringing up your child is one of the most important things you can do in life. What's the point of having children if you just want to dump them on someone else? Kay

> There were moments when my children were young that I wondered how successful I would be by now if I had continued with my career. But I see children rather like a marriage – a commitment, for richer, for poorer. Bonding in the early years is all-important, and that means being there for them, throughout the day and not just when it 'fits in' with work. Pat

Others believe they can do best for their child by continuing to earn so the child is brought up with the best of everything that money can buy, plus the love of a mother who is fulfilled in her career and in her role as parent.

> When I announced I was pregnant ... my father made it quite plain that he thought I should stay at home. When I discussed the issue with Tim, he was in no doubt: I would be impossible to live with if I gave up work. He knew that the monotony of staying at home would be difficult for me to cope with. He would not have liked to do it, and he did not see why I should either.
> from *Can You Have it All?*, Nicola Horlick (Macmillan)

If possible, leave your options open. Not everyone is cut out to be a housewife, however idyllic it might sound at first. You may find that after a few months at home with the baby, you are looking forward to returning to work.

Others who thought they were itching to get back to work suddenly find they want nothing more than to stay at home with the new member of their family.

Quality of life means different things to different people. Have a long, hard think about what will work best for you and your family.

> Both my husband and I have to work long hours to make ends meet. We pay a fortune for childcare, can't afford to

move to the bigger house we desperately need, and have a miserable quality of life. We have little time for the children – no wonder many of our friends have decided not to have any. Tessa

Can you give up work?

Whether or not you can give up work, even if you want to, will depend on many factors. Ask yourself:

- How much income will be coming into the home?
- What maternity leave arrangements are available?
- How do you feel about putting your career on hold and the effect this will have on your future prospects?
- How does your partner feel about you giving up paid work?
- How do you feel about losing your financial independence?
- How do you and your partner feel about a fall in your standard of living?
- How strongly do you feel that you or your partner should be major influences on your child's early life?
- How does your partner feel about staying home to allow you to return to work instead?

These are all questions that should be asked ideally in advance of planning to have a baby, so that you have a good idea of which options will suit you best. Possible solutions allowing you to stay at home while keeping your option to return to work open may include an employment/career break or, if you are eligible, a sabbatical.

Employment/career breaks

An employment/career break is an extended length of unpaid time – usually up to five years – spent away from work. This is sometimes known as a retainer scheme as the intention is for you to return to work for your employer in your old job, or one at a similar level. You may be required to undertake a regular refresher course, long-distance training or some other method of keeping up to date such as working a number of pre-agreed paid days per year (usually one to four weeks).

This scheme provides you with a formal way of leaving the workplace to look after your baby (for example until he or she starts nursery or primary school) without the worry of having to find a job or having to start again at a lower level of seniority than before. It

I thought staying at home would be easy compared to work. It wasn't. I hated being tied to the house and the baby. I soon realized I didn't have the strong maternal instincts I expected. I love my baby and wouldn't be without her. I just couldn't be a full-time mother. It would drive me mad. Jo

When my baby was six months old, an ex-colleague head-hunted me for a new, full-time job. Within two months I knew I had made a mistake. I loved the job, but hated missing my baby's development and hearing about his milestones second-hand. I was jealous of the childminder! In the end, we compromised and I went part-time for the best of both worlds. Kathy

A professional on ...
The life of a working mother

Don't feel guilty if you have to work, as long as you have done your best to provide an alternative safe, loving and stimulating environment for your child. I don't regret going back to work at all, although I couldn't imagine having to work full-time. It definitely makes me a better mother — more patient and devoted to my children on the days I am with them, with the knowledge that for a couple of days a week I have some time for myself. It's honed my self-discipline, time-management and general organizational skills. And the children have thrived on the lively and constant attention of our nanny on the days I am not there. After all she doesn't have to spend part of the day on chores, long telephone calls, ironing, washing and the like. So all in all, we all seem to be doing okay with a working mother in the family. A word of warning though — the price I have paid for working and having children is that I have virtually no free time. My evenings are spent picking up the pieces and collapsing exhausted on the sofa.

When things are getting really difficult, try to keep a perspective on the fact that it is just a phase, which will move on and get better. What will follow will be new, equally difficult challenges but at least it will be different and you will feel that you have mastered one tricky aspect of parenting. On a similar theme, just as my daughter's obsession with Spot was becoming totally intolerable she changed tack to worship Thomas the Tank Engine. I liked him even less than Spot but at least the stories were fresh and it was a few weeks before Thomas fatigue set in, at which point Winnie-the-Pooh made his entrance ...

Dr Patricia Macnair, GP, BBC Radio

may have a negative effect on future career prospects and will affect your pension, however.

A survey of over 900 companies in 1991 showed that 12 percent offered career breaks to selected staff, while a 1993 survey on behalf of New Ways to Work (an organization formed to help those who want to combine parenting and a career) found that availability of employment breaks in local government offices increased from 9 percent in 1990 to 22 percent in 1993.

Even if your employer does not have a formal employment/career break scheme, it may be possible to negotiate one in advance of planning to have a baby.

Sabbaticals

A sabbatical is a period of time off from work on top of annual leave, given essentially as a reward for lengthy service. A short sabbatical (e.g. one month) may be available after working for your employer for a relatively short period of time (say four years), while longer sabbaticals (six months to one year) may be offered to those who have worked continuously for the same employer for a longer period of time (perhaps 20 years). In some cases the sabbatical is paid and may be used as you wish. For the purposes of childcare, it is only likely to affect older men who are becoming fathers or older women who have pursued an active professional career before deciding to have a family. It may be possible to use sabbatical leave to provide an additional few months at home with your new baby on top of maternity or paternity leave, for example. Other employers stipulate that sabbatical leave must be used for a specific purpose such as further education or travel. It is estimated that around 20 percent of employers offer a formal sabbatical scheme. Where one is not available, it may be possible to negotiate one. Some sabbaticals are unpaid and may be arranged as a form of special leave.

Going back to work

A report commissioned on behalf of the Department for Education and Employment found that, in 1994, 59 percent of mothers were employed, compared with 70 percent of other women, 85 percent of fathers and 70 percent of other men. This was a significant increase from ten years previously, when a similar survey found that only 49 percent of mothers were employed. Increasing numbers of women

I work full-time now my son is in school, because I want to and can manage it, just. I respect all mothers' and fathers' wishes, however. Whatever they decide is best for their family, IS best. Annie

I realized soon after my baby was born that I just couldn't leave her with strangers. I was confident about returning to work beforehand, but as my maternity leave was coming to an end, I started to waver. When the crunch came, I couldn't do it. I had to refund some of my maternity pay but I didn't care. It was worth it to stay at home with my baby. When we sat down and worked out the difference between my lost income and what we would have paid in tax and childcare, we weren't that much worse off. Sam

are opting to combine working with bringing up a child. The greatest increase has occurred among women with a child under five years of age, who are university graduates and living with a partner. Between 1984 and 1994 women with children under the age of five increased the average length of their working week by five hours reflecting a growing trend towards full-time working. One of the key findings of this report was that, although children are being raised in more affluent surroundings as a result of their parents working, this is at the expense of spending increasingly less time with their parents. At the other end of the spectrum however, around a third of children are also growing up in a household where there is no full-time earner, and the report queried the effects this insecurity would have on the next generation of parents.

Those who strongly feel that mothers should stay at home and look after their babies frequently quote research – now felt to be flawed – that claimed children of working mothers achieved poor examination results and were twice as likely to fail GCSE examinations than children of mothers who stayed at home. This was guaranteed to trigger guilt trips, but at least eight other studies have found the opposite – that having a working mother increases a child's educational achievements. It is therefore important not to be swayed too much by either argument. If you want to have a baby and continue to work, you should not allow anyone to persuade you otherwise. Listen to your instincts and consider the practicalities to decide which is the best option for you and your family.

Be prepared for the initial feelings of guilt and sadness that most new mothers experience when first leaving their baby with someone else. Missing out on your child's major milestones – crawling, first word, first step – can be devastating, but can also help you to cherish the milestones you do manage to share with your child. Try to retain perspective by remembering that the first step seen by you is just as important – maybe even more so – than the first step taken a few hours previously but seen by someone else.

Preparing to go back to work

If you decide to go back to work, you need to think ahead and be prepared for all the implications. Ask yourself:

- How many hours do you want to work?
- Who is going to look after your child when you are at work?

- What time will you need to get up to wash, feed and clothe yourself and your baby?
- How much time (if any) will you need to get your baby and carer together?
- What time will you need to leave work to take over your baby's care again?
- How will you fit in essential tasks such as shopping for groceries (choose an au pair, nanny or childminder who is prepared to do this for you) and cleaning the house (consider getting a cleaner if you can afford it)?
- How much will you need to earn to cover costs of childcare, clothing, travel, tax, national insurance, pension and other deductions? Working this out will help you calculate how much you need to earn to make returning to work a viable option.
- Will financial considerations be less important if you are returning to work for the sake of your future career, because you love your job, or if you want to preserve your sanity or work confidence?
- How will you fit in breast-feeding if still applicable (expressing, freezing, lunch-time and tea-break feeds are all possibilities – see chapter 12)?

I lost all confidence in my ability to work after taking extended maternity leave for 52 weeks. In retrospect, I wish I had just taken the standard 18 weeks.
Julie

How family-friendly are British employers?

As a result of influence from the European community, British employers are becoming more family-friendly, although there is still a long way to go. In a 1997 survey of 1,000 professional, working mothers, 89 percent wanted to build more flexibility into their weekly schedule.

An extensive survey undertaken in 1996 on behalf of the Department For Education and Employment interviewed 1,311 representative employers and 2,051 new mothers (and their partners) who had had a baby in June 1996. The survey looked at the provision of four family-friendly work practices:

- extra statutory maternity benefits over and above the minimum requirements set by law
- availability of paternity leave
- employer contributions towards the cost of childcare
- flexible working options.

The results showed that overall, 92 percent of employers provided at least some form of family-friendly arrangements for their employees. Companies who did not offer additional benefits tended to be small private firms rather than large organizations.

Surprisingly, only 27 percent of companies surveyed offered additional benefits above those required by law around the time of childbirth, such as extended maternity leave, paternity leave or enhanced maternity pay.

Flexible working arrangements were available from as many as 71 percent of employers surveyed. The most common provision was for flexible working hours for part-time employees (41 percent) or full-time staff (36 percent). Around one in four (24 percent) allowed people to switch permanently from full-time to part-time work, while just over one in five (22 percent) had a scheme that enabled a temporary switch from full-time to part-time work. These options are likely to be most useful for women planning to have a baby and wanting to combine their career with spending more time at home caring for their new family. In addition, 15 percent of employers offered a non-standard working week for those wishing to remain working full-time, with weekly hours spread over four days rather than five for example. One in two mothers (52 percent) said their employer had a policy of allowing job sharing, but only a quarter were eligible to take this option up, and only one in ten (9 percent) had done so since having their baby.

Of the mothers interviewed for the survey, 65 percent said they had returned to work part-time and, of these, around a third had shifted down to working part-time from being full-time employed before having their baby. Three quarters of these were first-time mothers and some found they had to change employers in order to achieve their aim of working part-time.

More than three out of four companies (77 percent) did provide help towards the cost of childcare for employees returning to work afterwards, however, with 63 percent offering special leave schemes, 23 percent occasional working from home, 17 percent employment breaks and 9 percent making some financial contribution towards childcare costs. Only 2 percent of firms offered a workplace nursery, another 1 percent offered nursery places elsewhere and a further 2 percent provided a childcare allowance or vouchers.

More and more employers are starting to offer flexible work contracts, as they realize this is an important way of retaining trained and valued staff. This is actively encouraged by New Ways to

Work whose 1992 survey showed that two thirds of women in managerial grades in one organization wanted to reduce their working hours. As a direct result, the organization introduced job sharing and the concept of voluntarily reduced work time. As a result of parents requesting to work longer hours during school term times, the organization also set up a pilot scheme in which some workers could opt to work full-time during term-time but not at all for 13 weeks of school holidays each year. Salary and benefits are reduced accordingly. This flexibility is ideal for parents of school-aged children who wish to resume their full-time career once their children are older. Some employers will also allow career-break schemes and teleworking – i.e. working from home. All it requires is an element of vision and flexibility on the part of the employer.

Increased flexibility in the workplace was also supported at a summit of European Heads of State held in Luxembourg in November 1997, in which four main employment priorities were highlighted. These priorities involve a new culture of:

Entrepreneurship to make it easier to set up, finance and run a small business.

Employability to promote active benefit incentives, training and work experience.

Adaptability with renegotiation of work patterns, flexible working arrangements and reduced working time along with a framework in which those opting to work reduced hours should not be penalized in career progression or social-security entitlements.

Equal opportunity, so that men and women can reconcile their work and family commitments with dedicated career breaks and the right to parental leave and part-time work.

The Equal Opportunities Commission believes that for equality of opportunity to become reality, adequate childcare, parental leave and a family-friendly working environment are necessary. They have launched a campaign to initiate national discussion on the question of parental leave rights and how they should be implemented in the UK. More information is available from the EOC (see Resources, 244).

Find out in advance what is available from your place of work when thinking about having a baby, to see how this fits in with your working ideal. If your company has no plans to introduce flexible

After returning from maternity leave, I returned part-time to my job as a PR executive in a public relations firm and expected to work three-quarters of my previous working day. It was a total nightmare. Everyone expected me to be working just as hard as before and if I tried to walk out of the office early I received dirty looks from female as well as male colleagues who felt they were taking the brunt of my reduced hours. In the end, I quietly moved to another employer where, because I was starting from scratch as part-time, I managed to keep to my contracted hours without difficulty. Sara

ways of working, then contact New Ways to Work (see Resources, page 244) for information to give to your employer which may help to persuade them of the benefits to themselves as well as their staff.

Flexible working arrangements

For many women, returning to work part-time offers the best quality of life and has less of an impact on their work experience and career than spending a prolonged period of time away from the workplace.

Part-time work

The government defines a part-time worker as one who works fewer than 30 hours a week. According to New Ways to Work, two thirds of part-time employees work fewer than 21 hours per week with an average of 18 hours for women and 16 for men. Part-time work is becoming more common. The number of people working part-time has doubled over the last 20 years and now makes up around a quarter of the workforce. Forty percent of all females who work do so part-time, compared with only 6 percent of men, and overall eight out of ten part-time workers are women. Those who work part-time do not always do so through choice, but as a way of balancing the need to work and the need to stay at home – it is an obvious option, and often one that is easiest to arrange. It is estimated that one in three workers will be part time by the year 2000. Some employers have introduced an innovative scheme in which workers work part-time on an alternative week basis. It may also be possible to negotiate working one week on and one week off, perhaps with another part-time worker so your hours dovetail almost like a job-share.

If you are making the decision to go part-time from full-time, you will need to consider carefully the implications for your contractual rights such as reduced salary, entitlements to paid holidays, sick leave, pension and – importantly – future maternity benefits and leave if you decide to have another baby. You may also need to consider the effect on staff discounts and share options if you currently receive these. Against this you need to balance the benefits of spending more time with your child, lower levels of work-related stress and – often – increased job satisfaction.

If you opt to work part-time, you also need to ensure that you don't regularly work more hours than you should because of continuing work pressure. Have a word with other part-time employees in your company doing similar work to yourself to find out how they have fared.

> After having my first baby, I decided to go from being a full-time hospital nurse to a part-time 'bank' nurse available to cover leave and sickness. Bank nurses were in short supply, and I could pick and choose the hours I worked, as well as gaining wider experience by working on different wards. I tend to work three days and one night a week – usually my husband's half-day so he can babysit. It works well. I'm with my daughter most of the week, have job satisfaction still spend weekends as a family at home. Whenever I feel tired, or my child is ill, I just tell the hospital I'm unavailable. Sylvia

Job sharing

Job sharing is where two people voluntarily share the responsibilities of a single full-time job – usually a skilled, senior management or professional one – by each holding a permanent part-time position. Time worked does not necessarily have to be equal, as long as pay, holidays and other benefits are divided up between the two pro rata. Job share options are mainly used by women with family responsibilities – often on returning from maternity leave – although a few men are starting to take advantage of job sharing, too, so they can spend more time caring for their children. While job sharing usually works successfully, you need to have good communication with your sharer and may find you get less job satisfaction if you have to share the credit for joint achievements.

Some job sharing women have found they work longer hours than contracted for and are expected to receive work telephone calls while at home and supposedly off-duty. When considering flexible work packages on offer from your employer, you need to do your homework and talk to others who have taken these options up in order to weigh up the pros and cons of each. At least one in four employers offer a job share scheme but they are not widely taken advantage of. According to the 1995 Labour Market Survey, such posts were held by less than 1 percent of those surveyed. Job sharing is likely to increase, as professional bodies and trade unions have started to set up registers that aim to match potential sharers who can then apply for certain jobs together as a preformed team.

> I opted to reduce my working week from five days to three, once I had my baby. By not going into the office at all for two days, I thought I would manage to keep work at bay. I started to get more and more calls at home however, so in the end I installed an answer-machine which said I was off-duty and unavailable. The message soon got through. Felicity

As a new mother, I job-share a full-time post as a general practitioner – with my husband. We both wanted to share bringing up our baby, and this way one of us is always at home. It sometimes seems as if we live for our job as one or other of us is frequently on duty at night. We stipulated at the beginning that we would always take holidays together however – having two job sharers away at the same time is no different than having one full-time person away, after all. We had to work hard to fight our corner however – our partners seemed to think job sharers should cover for each other's absence. Ann

Voluntary reduced work time

Voluntary reduced work time (known as V-time) allows you to stay in the same job and voluntarily reduce the number of hours you work in exchange for reduced pay and benefits. You trade a given amount of income – usually between 5 and 50 percent – for the equivalent time off from your normal full-time working week. This can be for a short-term period, say six months, or an extended length of time such as five years, after which you have the opportunity (and right) to return to work full-time. The exact number of hours worked can be flexible so you can work five days that are shorter than normal, spread your hours over, for example, four days rather than five, or take a block of time off at certain times of the year (e.g. during term-time) and work full-time in between. The concept of V-time is well developed in the United States, and is starting to become more popular in the UK. A common problem seems to be that although your hours are reduced, your responsibilities and work allocation may not be. You may find you end up working harder as you try to fit everything into your reduced hours and this is something you need to discuss with your employer and colleagues when thinking of opting for voluntarily reduced work time to ensure that it does not happen.

> **I negotiated to return from maternity leave and work on a V-time basis for as long as I wanted before resuming full-time employment. This made all the potentially difficult decisions about returning to work very easy. I worked five mornings a week and left my baby with a childminder close to my place of work. As she has got older, I've slowly started to increase the number of hours I work.** Jane

Term-time working

When your children are older, term-time working may be an option worth considering – it is also useful for those whose partner is a teacher as it provides an opportunity to spend more time together at home as a family unit. Term-time working lets you remain in your usual job, either part-time or full-time, on a permanent contract, but means you have the right to unpaid leave during the school holidays – around 13 weeks a year. Some of this time off will be taken as paid annual leave, but the excess time – an average of eight weeks – may be taken as unpaid leave. In some cases, you may be required to go into the office on a regular basis – for example one day a week – but this significantly reduces the time for which you need to make alternative childcare arrangements when schools are on holiday. The 1995 Labour Market Survey found that 7.4 percent of female employees and 1.4 percent of males worked on a term-time only basis. This option is becoming increasingly popular as a way of attracting women to return to the workplace after taking a few years off to bring up their young family.

Annual hours

An annual hours scheme allows to you work a set number of hours per year, depending on the needs of the business, rather than working a set number of hours a week. The system is primarily designed to give the employer flexibility in asking staff to work at short notice during busy times, and may include a need for working unsociable hours. The annual hours option is less likely to be helpful for new parents.

Going back to work full-time

For some new parents, going back to work full-time is necessary or desirable. Some flexibility may still be possible however, especially if your company runs a flexitime scheme.

Flexitime

Flexitime schemes allow you to choose when you start and finish work – usually within a certain daily time span – as long as you work a requisite number of hours per month. Flexitime only usually applies to full-time workers but is useful as it allows you to plan your working day according to the needs of your childcare. In an example provided by New Ways to Work, a mother and father were able to use their flexitime so that one started work late and could drop their baby off at the nursery/childminder, while the other parent started work earlier so they could leave in time to collect the child from nursery at the end of the day. It is often also possible to arrange flexileave so you can make up time spent at home – for example if your usual childcarer is unavailable, or your child is ill – at a later date. The Labour Market Survey in 1995 found that 11 percent of employees overall were able to work flexible hours.

New Ways to Work can provide fact sheets detailing the options for flexible work patterns, including:

My husband is a teacher and has always worked on a term-time basis. I stayed at home until our baby was two years old and could attend a local nursery. My husband was able to drop him off and collect him, and was always there in the holidays so I could return to work full-time. Penny

I work as an account director for a medical publishing company and liaise with clients as well as writing copy for projects. When my baby was born, I negotiated working from home for four days a week and just going in one day a week. I keep in contact with clients and the office via phone, fax and e-mail, and arrange my client meetings for the day I'm at the office. My mother is happy to act as childminder one day a week and the arrangement works brilliantly. Jessica

- part-time work
- job sharing
- voluntary reduced work time
- flexitime
- term-time working
- annual hours
- career breaks
- sabbaticals
- working from home.

The fact sheets are free of charge (just send them an A4-sized SAE plus postage) and summarise each flexible work option plus its pros and cons for both staff and employers. They also provide guidance on how to negotiate flexible work contracts, even in situations where they are not offered by an employer. For contact details, see Resources, page 244.

Could you work from home?

Working from home, either for an employer or as a self-employed individual, is an ideal option for those who want to combine childcare with continuing to work. The obvious advantages are that it saves travel time, allows flexibility as you can usually have time off during the day if necessary and make it up in the evening when your child is asleep. Some may feel this is not an advantage as work may end up taking over your evenings; it does allow more flexibility though. Your home costs (telephone, electricity, heating and postage bills) will be higher but employers may help to meet these expenses. Home backup is essential to help with childcare. Don't be tempted to look after your baby yourself as well as working, otherwise you will find yourself overwhelmed by the conflicting needs of a new baby, domestic chores and work deadlines.

Isolation and lack of motivation can be a problem, although the motivation of being able to stay at home and interact with your young children when you wish is more than enough for many satisfied home workers. There are benefits for your employer, too, as interestingly several studies show that home workers are 20-45 percent more productive than their office counterparts. This increase in productivity is often effortless as you can easily gain an hour a day from reduced travel and no time spent on office gossip. According to New Ways to Work, it may also be because home-based work is planned, managed and broken into measurable chunks. If you feel your job could be performed from home in whole or in part, it is worth talking to your employer before deciding to have a baby to see if you can set things up in advance. Some organizations already have a policy allowing certain employees to work from home while others may be open to change.

Some workers use up-to-date information technology (computer networks, e-mail) to keep in touch with their employer's office and this is known as teleworking. Although start-up costs may be high, teleworking helps to cut employer's overheads and is becoming increasingly acceptable.

Could you work self-employed from home?

For many people, being self-employed and working from home is the equivalent of having it all. As long as you are reasonably certain of a regular income, and don't mind the uncertainty of whether work and money will continue to flow, this option is well worth considering. Anyone with a skill to sell could feasibly be self-employed and working from home: a writer, designer, craftsperson, consultant, accountant, computer programmer, artist, teacher, researcher, indexer, word processor, editor, proofreader, party organizer, therapist, book keeper, a bed & breakfast proprietor or childminder to name but a few. Here are some points to think about if you are considering this option so that you can be on hand to enjoy your baby regularly, continue breast-feeding and keep an eye on whoever is looking after your child:

- You will need to assess your skills and how they might be used to provide a regular income.
- Work out how you can market your skills to potential customers.
- Think about whether you have the self-discipline to work regularly from home – you need to be self-motivated, self-disciplined, a self-starter, well-organized and a good communicator who is able to balance work and domestic commitments.
- Consider how will you feel about the isolation and loneliness of mostly working on your own?
- Work out how much space you will need and whether your home is adequate for your needs.
- Estimate start-up costs and how much money you need to bring in

I was able to continue doing a certain amount of work as my husband's 'office backup', since we were working together in our own home-based company, until I could get back to travelling and tutoring (as a freelance trainer) myself. At that point (when number two was starting school), we took to advertising for 'intermittent minders' and were incredibly lucky with almost all of those who came. Girls retaking their NNEB finals at the local college of FE were particularly valuable, as their times were as flexible as our needs, and they had good basic training and were motivated. DO take up and check references thoroughly.
Cecilia

As a writer, I already worked from home. I thought it would be easy to continue doing the same when the baby was here. I found I couldn't concentrate however – when he was awake, I wanted to be with him, and when he was asleep I worried about cot death and therefore had him asleep (in his basket) in the office with me. But this meant I had to switch the phone off in case it woke him so my contacts – magazine and newspaper commissioning editors – couldn't get hold of me easily. I had to do something, and quick. I decided to have a live-in au pair – the best decision I ever made. She's brilliant.
Sarah

each month and whether or not you can realistically manage this.

- Check out the competition: are your skills unique, in good demand and saleable or is the market place already saturated with what you have to offer?
- Talk to your bank manager, your bank's branch business advisor and an accountant.
- Consult your local Training & Enterprise Council and Trading Standards Office for advice.
- Seek advice from an accountant on the implications of using part of your home for work.
- Contact your tax office for advice about changing your tax code.
- Keep an eye on the threshold income at which you will need to register for VAT.
- Seek advice from your local planning office. The right to work from home is enshrined in Planning Policy Guidance Note number 4, 'Industrial and Commercial Development and Small Firms' although not all local planning departments and enforcement officers are aware of this. In some instances you do need to gain planning permission if you are changing the overall character of your property as a single dwelling.
- Obtain information from self-help organizations such as Ownbase – the national association for home-based working (see Resources, page 245).

If you decide to work self-employed from home you must ensure you can clear adequate time and space – it is no good expecting to fit in work with domestic chores and baby care unless you are dabbling and do not need to rely on a regular income.

For more information about working from home, contact OwnBase and Better Business (see Resources, page 244).

A professional on ...
The pros and cons of working from home

At the time that I organised my working life so that I could work from home, I did not realise how well it would lend itself to motherhood. I had become a freelance for other reasons: a need to extricate myself from the 8am-8pm routine; being fed up dealing with office politics... So I was pleased when it also suited my new family life.

However, certain pitfalls soon became apparent. My job involves the need for long stretches of concentration, which can be difficult with a baby or toddler around... toddlers in particular do not understand that Mummy needs to be left alone for a couple of hours, their needs are usually immediate. No matter how good your partner or home-help are, they are still not Mummy. So the habit that I fell into was to work whenever junior was asleep. Fine when he was having naps all day, but as these petered out I would start work when he went to bed in the evening. After a while, this made my 8am-8pm office hours seem like the easy option.

I have become a past master at fitting in small jobs as I go along, usually with a small child balanced on my hip. I have fallen into the trap of using videos as entertainment on the odd occasion – just to have half an hour to get a job done – and I have to be very strict about working on projects on the days he goes to playschool.

I know many women who have elected to remain at the office as they did not believe they could handle the juggling act of a small child at home while freelancing, however for me this was definitely the right decision. A year and a half from now, my little boy will be starting full-time school and I am so glad to have had the opportunity to spend these early years with him – even if it has been a tiny bit fraught from time to time!

Suzannah Olivier, nutritionist and author of *What Should I Feed My Baby?* (Weidenfeld & Nicolson)

Gay parenting: Sharing the work
by **Lisa Saffron**

Children need parents who take an interest in them and are willing to prioritize their needs. In so many heterosexual couples, the fathers have little time for their children. They're out at work full-time while the mothers do all the juggling of work and childcare. When lesbians have children, they tend not to mimic heterosexual divisions of labour. It is not common for one partner in a lesbian couple to take the role of dependent wife and primary childcarer while the other goes out to work. Lesbian couples are a positive role model of egalitarian parenting. Inequalities in lesbian relationships inevitably exist as a result of class, financial and personality differences, but usually both partners in a lesbian couple share the tasks of earning a living, caring for children and performing household chores.

Gill Dunne, a researcher at Cambridge University compared lesbian couples raising children with heterosexual parents. The lesbian couples had fairly equal involvement in domestic work and childcare because they were willing to create a balance between paid work and home life. There were less extreme differences in the time they each spent in paid work than there were for the heterosexual couples where the man spent most of his time at work.

American research studies have also found this to be true. One study by Charlotte Patterson (1995) shows co-mothers (the mother without the biological connection) spending more time caring for their children than heterosexual birth fathers who live with their wives. In another North American study, David Flaks and his colleagues (1995) compared 15 lesbian couples with 15 heterosexual couples, all of whom had children by donor insemination. The lesbian couples were more aware of the skills needed for effective parenting than the heterosexual couples. They were better able to recognize problems in parenting and to imagine solutions for them. The heterosexual couples did less well in this comparison because the fathers performed poorly in this test. All the mothers, whether lesbian or heterosexual, were aware of good parenting skills.

Cases in point

Margaret, working lesbian mother

My partner, Cecilia, and I both work full-time as social work team managers. I still have all the guilt about being a working mother but work is important to me. It's part of my identity. I've always wanted a career as well as a family. I couldn't be at home full-time with a baby. Although it's great having time with Cecilia and the children on holidays, I'm happy working full-time. If I worked part-time, I wouldn't get the same opportunities at work and we couldn't afford to live where we do.

Anna tries to work part time

My ideal working situation is to work four days a week during school hours so I can take the children to and from school. I find full-time work too much, though of course, it's necessary to be able to earn enough to have a reasonable standard of life. You need time for household chores and for the children. I want to be there to pick the children up from school when they're little and to be there as they get home when they're older. There have been times I've come home late from work and Kate's already been at home for a few hours and she's past discussing her day with me – I miss out.

Jude, lesbian mother with two daughters, aged 10 and 14

My partner, Linda, and I have always shared the childcare equally and have taken turns working full-time and part-time. I had six months' paid maternity leave after Kate was born. Then both Linda and I worked half-time. We literally divided the week in half between work and childcare. I was working as an officer of the trade union and Linda was working for a homeless persons' organization. We were both earning about the same amount and both having time on our own with Kate. That was particularly important for Linda as the non-biological mother.

Chapter 5:
Domestic Support Structures

We lived in a high-rise flat in London, which I felt wasn't appropriate for bringing up a young child. We decided to leave London and moved to a lovely house in the country. Our son was born 11 months later. Sarah

When I discovered I was pregnant, we realized we would have to move home. We had a steep flight of stairs to climb to get to our flat which would have been difficult to negotiate with a buggy. Kate

When you want to become a parent, it is important to think ahead about the domestic support structures you will need to have in place by the time your baby is born.

Your home

One of the most important considerations is where you live. The nesting instinct often drives women to consider moving house when planning to have a baby – hence the old saying, 'New home, new baby'. Things to consider include:

- Is your home large enough for a new addition?
- How isolated are you? Would you be happy to stay at home all day with a baby if living in an isolated dwelling? If not, will you have ready access to childcare?
- Do you have room for a live-in nanny/au pair? If you opt for an au pair, will he or she have easy access to transport and English lessons?
- Do you have/need a garden?
- Could you get in and out of your home easily with a pram/pushchair?
- How well do you know people locally? Is there anyone local you could call on in an emergency?
- How close are you to amenities such as buses, trains, shops, a doctor's surgery and a chemist? Would you have access to nappy delivery services for example (Boots the Chemist have a mail order nappy service)?
- How far/long will you and/or your partner have to travel to work and what implications will this have for your childcare and other domestic arrangements?

Early help

In an ideal world, you need full-time help for at least a week or two after you come home from hospital from having your baby, and preferably for the first month. Many women are able to call on a relative.

Other options to think about include your partner – can he/she have time off work to help you for at least the first two weeks? You may also have close friends and neighbours who will rally around to help.

If you can afford it, employing a paid mother's help, nanny or maternity nurse for two to six weeks is another way of helping you get back on your feet and into a new routine when you have the needs of a new baby to consider. A good maternity nurse will usually be booked up well in advance. If you decide you would like one you need to start looking almost as soon as you are pregnant – either advertise in *The Lady* magazine, or register with an agency (to whom you will also have to pay a finder's fee). A maternity nurse will help you to get your baby into a routine while you are recovering from the pregnancy and delivery. She will also sleep in the baby's room and meet their needs at night if you wish, only bringing the baby in to you to breast-feed. This approach will not suit everyone, however, as for many new mums having their baby in bed with them is one pleasure they would not want to give up (see page 179).

Domestic upkeep

A new baby is a full-time occupation. If you currently manage all your housework, window cleaning, shopping and gardening yourself, you will need to think ahead as to how these tasks can be accomplished once you have had a baby. If you are planning to stay at home, you may like to try and continue with all these. If you are returning to work, however, you may no longer be able to fit these tasks in so easily as your evenings and weekends will now start to revolve around the baby. This is one of the many hidden costs that can arise from starting a family, but if you can afford it, think about having domestic help to do routine cleaning chores around the home – this will make life far easier once you have a baby.

Childcare

If you decide to return to work, you need to consider carefully who will look after your baby. This is one of the most important decisions you will make as you are literally entrusting the life and wellbeing of

I wanted our baby cared for in her own environment, and realized we would need an extra bedroom for a live-in nanny or au pair when I returned to work. We therefore postponed starting a family until we could afford to move house, after my husband's promotion. Jennifer

I had my first baby by Caesarean and was grateful when my mum offered to come and stay while I was in hospital. She was still here six weeks later – we couldn't have managed without her. Helen

A professional says ...

It is reported that when the Duke of Wellington, who was a talented amateur musician, first joined the army, he broke his violin across his knee, remarking that no man can serve two masters. There is no more exacting master than a baby. Now that conceiving a child is no longer by and large a matter of instinct and accident, and in an overpopulated world in which many of us find life a burden rather than a privilege, it is irresponsible to reproduce without having first, like most of our fellow creatures, set up conditions in which a baby can grow and develop to realize his or her full potential. These conditions include in the early months of life the focused devotion of either the baby's natural mother or someone prepared to step into her shoes.

Professor John A. Davies, paediatrician

one of your most treasured and vulnerable possessions to someone else. That person may well be a total stranger about whom you know very little, so it is vital to check their qualifications (if any) and to always take up references.

Conflicting feelings

However strong your intentions to return to your career soon after having the baby, you will find yourself asking soul-searching questions about how you can possibly go out of the house all day and leave your precious bundle with someone else. Some mothers worry that this may even be harmful to their child's development. Studies are reassuring however, suggesting that children in day-care nurseries receive more stimulation, perform better, have greater social skills and are more out-going, independent and self-aware than children who are looked after solely by their mother all day. This may reflect the fact that new mothers have little or no training on how to stimulate their child in the early years and rely on love and instinct. Nannies and nursery school teachers on the other hand have some relevant formal training. These findings help to take away the guilt of deciding to return to work, and also suggest that if you do decide to stay at home, you may need to take steps to ensure your child regularly interacts with other adults and children.

As long as a child receives affection, warmth and plenty of attention it does not seem to matter if the mother is not the primary carer. Mothers who work have been shown to spend as much time in child-orientated activities as mothers who are caring for their child full-time, as housewives have other domestic and social commitments that fill a lot of their hours. Interestingly, labour-saving devices and changes in lifestyle mean that modern day mothers who work full-time actually spend twice as many hours interacting with their children than non-employed mothers did in the early 1960s.

Therefore, if you do decide to go back to work, the message is: don't feel guilty but take positive steps to interact with your child as much as possible. Although it has become something of a cliché, the concept of 'quality' time is all-important. If the mother is happy in her choice – whether it is to work or to stay at home – this seems to be more important for her child's development than whether or not she is the primary carer. A fulfilled woman is likely to be a better mother than one racked with frustration or guilt.

Who will look after your baby?

It may seem premature to be thinking about childcare when you aren't even pregnant, but it is useful to know about the various options for when the time comes. Thinking ahead about the best option for you – and what is available locally – may play a part in helping you to decide when the time is right for you to start your family. You may also need to register for a place at a nursery, with a maternity nurse or a childminder almost as soon as you know you are pregnant.

Good childcare is usually oversubscribed and will be booked up well in advance. Increasing numbers of employers now provide an on-site crèche, childcare vouchers, help with out-of-hours childcare if you need to work unsociable hours, or a childcare bonus payment to encourage trained staff to return to work after having a baby. Although they will not usually cover all childcare costs, they can ease the financial burden considerably. Different companies offer different amounts and have different criteria for eligibility depending on position and the length of time you have been employed, for example. It is therefore worth finding out whether you would be entitled to any of these job perks if you were to become pregnant.

Several childcare options are available, and in order to work out which is best for you and your family, you will need to ask yourself questions such as:

- How much can you afford to spend on childcare before it becomes uneconomical for you to work? (For childcare costs, see chapter 6.)
- Do you want your baby cared for in your own home?
- Are you happy for your child to spend the day in someone else's environment?
- Do you want the childcare to be based near your office, your husband's or partner's office or near to home (taking into account which is most convenient for dropping off and collecting your baby and/or breast-feeding)?
- How stable would the arrangements be, and how reliable would the carer be?
- How much individual attention will your child receive?
- If you are considering a childminder, how many other children would be making demands on his/her time?

I knew my employer paid extra towards the cost of childcare if I had to work overtime, but I didn't realize I was eligible for childcare vouchers as a long-term employee as well. In fact no one else seemed aware of this either, until I went through my staff handbook and found the small print. Several of us have started claiming the vouchers now – don't rely on your employer to tell you what you are eligible for. Ask and find out for yourself.

Pamela

- What facilities would you expect to be available for broadening your child's experience of life?
- Do you want your child to interact with other children in a childminder's home or a nursery?
- Do you have room for a nanny or au pair to live in?
- Can you afford a trained nanny?
- Would you feel happy entrusting your baby's care to a young, untrained au pair?
- What backup arrangements would you have in the event that either your child or their carer is sick?
- How easy is it to ensure compliance with any strong ideas you have on the way your child is disciplined, educated or fed?

Whoever looks after your child, seek advice on safety in the home, employment/agreement contracts and any additional insurance cover you may need for your home and car.

Leaving your baby can be a complete wrench at the beginning. You will find yourself imagining all sorts of horrors and accidents, and of course it is difficult to believe that anyone can care for your baby as much as you do yourself. However, despite media scare stories, most babies thrive with a trained carer and come to no harm. It is important to ensure that there is continuity of care for your child's stability however, as far as possible.

The father as carer
Sometimes, it makes sense for the father-to-be to consider leaving paid employment rather than the mother. Whether or not a mother and father can swap traditional childcaring roles depends on a number of factors, such as:

- how much they both enjoy their jobs
- the relative income potential of both partners
- the relative career potential of both partners
- who enjoys being at home with the children most
- the relative costs of childcare
- whether or not the father (or mother) is worried about the unconventionality of the arrangement
- whether or not the father is worried about his image as main childcarer.

One important factor is that while there are strong support groups for mothers in most communities, a father-carer may find it hard to join them.

> As a female doctor married to an accountant, I felt I couldn't put my career on hold – I was too far up the ladder to fall off. My husband was feeling jaded with work and no longer enjoyed dealing with demanding clients. It was an obvious decision for him to stay home and look after the baby. After a few months, he even managed to set up his own part-time work at home – new tax self-assessment rules meant many people needed help filling out their tax forms. The next logical step was to get an au pair to help look after the baby and do light housework. People laugh, but I had no qualms about leaving my husband at home with our au pair – we chose one that was male! My husband was always there at home in case any problems arose. Deborah

Relatives
Many families rely on close relatives to help look after children and this is often one of the most satisfactory arrangements for all concerned. A loving grandparent or aunt will provide a warm, stable environment for your baby while you go to work.

Friends
If you pay a friend to look after your child in their own home, then they will need to be registered as a childminder. Many parents arrange to look after each other's children without payment however. If this is the case, and you intend relying on a friend to look after your child while you are at work, you will need to sort out in advance any strong views you have on how a child should be brought up and how emergencies (e.g. sick child or carer) are to be managed so that your friendship does not come under strain.

Mother's helps
A mother's help is usually a young, unqualified person who will help with childcare and light housework in exchange for a relatively small fee. The direct cost of employment may be offset against accommodation and food for those willing to live in. You would not usually expect to leave your child alone with a mother's help for any length of time – they are literally an extra pair of hands to watch your

My earnings were twice my husband's and we knew from the start that it made sense for me to go back to work. We agonized for ages about childcare arrangements. In the end, we decided it would be better for Jonathan to become a househusband. He got many odd looks at the playgroup, and when taking the baby for his immunizations at the surgery. Men think differently from women, however. I found it irritating when I'd sometimes get home to find housework undone, and dinner not planned because they'd been playing in the garden all day. In the end we got a cleaner in two mornings a week. It saved our marriage. Jules

I enjoy being a househusband and getting to know our son, but I sense strange looks when I take him to the doctor's, and feel awkward when taking him to the mother and toddler group. Richard

If you have a good relationship with your own mother, and she is intelligent and tolerant, she can be a huge help and comfort, even down the phone. On the other hand, you sometimes have to make your own choice between different bits of advice! Cecilia

child while you get on with your other responsibilities at home. Mother's helps from Australia and New Zealand seem to be the most popular.

Au pairs

An au pair is a young person aged between 17 and 27 – female or male – from a foreign country who has decided to act as a mother's help in exchange for accommodation, food, pocket money and an insight into British family life, most often while they improve their English language skills. An au pair usually has no training or qualifications and will help with light duties around the house, including childcare, but is not usually expected to have sole responsibility for a child/children – especially a baby – for any length of time. They typically work five hours a day, five days a week. Occasionally older au pairs may have some training as nurses or they may be medical students working to improve their English (the international medical language). They are often known as an 'au pair plus' and may be entrusted with extra childcare responsibilities and baby-sitting. They will also usually work longer hours (seven hours a day, five days a week).

Hours and conditions of employment will be strictly laid down by the au pair agency, and their stay with you will typically be between six months and one year. You are usually expected to give an au pair two days off per week, including time to attend an English class. An au pair will help with light domestic chores such as shopping, ironing, dusting, vacuuming, laundry and helping to prepare food. The more time you expect her to spend on housework however, the less time she will be available for quality interaction with your child.

> We now only opt for an au pair from Slovakia or the Czech Republic. They are very family orientated and do not expect to go partying every night. I've heard many horror stories about au pairs from France, Italy, Spain and Germany, but have had no problems with any of our [eastern European] girls. Debbie

An au pair may have poor English-language skills which may in turn affect your own child's language development. On the other hand they can help to expose a young child to the sounds of a foreign language at an early age, which may make learning that language easier in the future.

An au pair from an EU country does not need a work permit and can stay with you for as long as mutually agreed. An au pair from outside the EU will need a written invitation from you (via the employing agency) to obtain a work visa from the British Embassy in his/her country. This will be valid for a maximum of two years. The au pair will also need to register with the local police station for which a fee must be paid and two passport photos provided.

Nannies

Most nannies have undertaken a period of training to gain a qualification (from the Nursery Nurse Examination Board or equivalent) and are therefore more aware of the needs (health, safety, nutrition, education, play) of a young baby or child than many childminders. A few nannies do not have a qualification but have gained hands-on experience in childcare with other families. You will need to decide how much importance you attach to both training and experience and choose your nanny accordingly.

A nanny will take full care of your baby or child from any age, and can either live in or out depending on how much space you have and your individual requirements. Nannies are more expensive than au pairs and childminders, although some of the direct costs are offset by accommodation and food if they live in. If your nanny is not registered as self-employed, then as her employer you will be responsible for paying her tax and national insurance as well. It may be possible to share a full-time nanny with another mother to share costs while you both go to work part- or possibly full-time.

As well as looking after your child, a nanny will help with light domestic work related to your child, such as looking after your infant's laundry, bedroom and toys and preparing your child's meals. A nanny will not usually do any other form of housework as their main role is to provide quality infant care.

Finding a nanny through a nanny employment agency in the Yellow Pages is expensive as you have to pay their finding fee, too. One of the most popular ways of finding a nanny is to place an advert in *The Lady* magazine.

> I came to the conclusion that the best option for me would be to employ a nanny. It would give me the greatest flexibility and mean that I did not have to worry about dropping the baby off in the morning or collecting in the evening. I could see that there would be

Today it seems socially acceptable for a women to have both a career and a family. The 'nanny' is no longer the province of the upper class and I have heard many young mothers say they like to see their children for an hour or two before bedtime each day, feeling their children are adequately looked after. Many women, like me, feel this is totally wrong.
Pat

**a problem with all the other options if the baby was ever sick. It
might only be a heavy cold and a slight temperature, but in those
circumstances it would be difficult to put the baby in the car and
drop her off with a childminder or at a nursery.**
From *Can You Have it All?*, Nicola Horlick (Macmillan)

Childminder

A childminder is someone who looks after your child in their own
home, for a fee, which means that your child is away from their own
environment during this time. The childminder must be registered
with the local social services department, who will have a list of
those available in your area. Personal recommendation from another
satisfied parent is one of the best ways to find one, however, so ask
around well in advance of needing one.

Each childminder is only allowed responsibility for a certain
number of children of particular ages at any one time, and the good
ones are usually fully booked. It can therefore take several months to
find a suitable childminder in your area. A childminder often has
young children of his/her own and can provide a warm, family
atmosphere in which your baby will gain experience of being with
other children. Costs are not usually high, but you will need to make
time to drop your child off at the minder's and collect them again at
the end of their stay. And you will usually need to stay at home to
look after your child yourself if he or she is ill. As the childminder
can only look after a certain number of children and has committed
herself to caring for your child, you will probably still be expected to
pay a half fee for times when your child would usually be present but
is off sick (or on holiday) instead. No fee is paid if the childminder is
ill or on holiday, however. It is important to ensure that you like the
childminder you choose for your child, and that you share similar
views on smoking, discipline, play and nutrition.

If you want to work from home, becoming a childminder is an
option you may wish to consider. Contact the under-fives section of
your local social services department for an information pack on
minimum requirements for registering.

Nurseries and Crèches

There is little difference between a crèche and a nursery apart from
the name, although a crèche tends to be a nursery provided by an
employer or event organizer as an extra facility for its staff/customers.

A workplace crèche has the advantage of your child being close by during the day (ideal for breast-feeding) and of not requiring further travel on top of your usual commute. You will need ideally to be able to drive (or walk) to work, as carrying a baby or infant on the underground, or a crowded bus or train during the rush hour is not a pleasant option for either parent or child.

A workplace crèche will usually be open during normal work hours, but childcare staff may not have any specific training. Non-workplace nurseries are usually open from 8 or 8.30am until around 5 or 6pm Monday to Friday. All staff are trained and there must be at least one adult to care for every three children under the age of two. A nursery school, which provides an element of education and an introduction to pre-primary school, will usually only take children from the age of two or three onwards. Prices vary quite significantly, so work out your budget in advance to see what you can afford.

Each nursery and crèche is registered with local social services which ensures a certain minimum standard, but some are better than others. In general, a nursery/crèche provides a fun, action-packed, socially stimulating environment in which your child can learn and interact with other children and adults. Your child will not be able to attend if ill, so you must have alternative arrangements (e.g. a relative or flexitime) in place for these occasions. You will not have to make alternative arrangements at short notice as you might have to with a childminder, who may not always be available or who may become ill, however. Always check security and safety arrangements (for example how easy might it be for a stranger to enter the nursery or for your child to wander off?).

The Daycare Trust provides briefing papers that highlight the key features of successful childcare (see Resources, page 245, for contact details).

A professional says ...

For a woman to attempt to supplement the family income or to live up to other responsibilities means handing over more of the daily care of her baby to someone else – necessarily without the same degree of commitment – and so to forfeit to some degree what is normally her own pleasure in fulfilling her maternal instincts and to risk depriving her baby of the consistent relationship with its 'carer' which maternal preoccupation normally provides.
Professor John A. Davies, paediatrician

Chapter 6:
Financial Implications of Having a Baby[2]

by **Siobhan Carolan**

Having children is probably the most expensive decision the average family (2.4 children, estimated income per household of £20,000 per annum) will ever make. The typical cost of rearing a child from conception to 18 years is approximately £100,000 and this does not include the cost of private education, private health or dental care. If these costs are included in the equation the amount could easily rise to as much as £175,000-£200,000.

A child is a major drain on household expenses from before the baby is born until well after they are grown and ready to leave home. It is tempting to rush out and buy everything you think you might need as soon as the pregnancy test is positive, but it is best to wait several months until the pregnancy is well established and there is less risk of a miscarriage. This way you are also more likely to catch the sales and to obtain some of the items you need at a reduced cost.

While everyone naturally wants the best for their baby, this doesn't mean you have to buy everything new or from a designer range – unless of course you can afford it. It is often surprising how much equipment you can borrow from friends and relatives too – cots, baby baths and stair/door gates are often kept and in good order. It is vital to buy a new cot mattress for each baby however as this may help to reduce the risk of cot death. It is also advisable not to buy a second-hand car seat or infant carrier as you cannot be sure it hasn't been dropped and damaged or even been involved in a car accident which might have weakened it. Never fit a car seat unless you have the manufacturer's full fitting instructions.

Most parents should budget the equivalent of at least one month's take-home pay for buying all the basic one-off equipment needed during a baby's first year (excluding nappies and food).

---

[2] All costs are relevant at time of going to press

The items listed on the charts on the next three pages
are basic essentials you will need to provide for a baby
in its first year.

0-3 months

Infant carrier or car seat with head-support

Carrycot and/or baby sling

Carrycot bedding: new mattress plus at least four cotton sheets and four blankets (no pillow until 12 months); night light; nursery thermometer; baby monitor

Muslin squares or bibs for feeding

Three nursing bras, breast-pads, breast cups to catch excess milk; battery-operated breast pump; bags to store or freeze breast milk; 1 special bottle that holds bag of expressed milk; 2 nipple-shaped teats to feed expressed milk when necessary (boil or use sterilizing tablets to clean)

If bottle feeding: sterilizer, 6 teats and bottles; bottle brush; formula milk; consider bottle warmer

Disposable nappies; barrier cream, wipes impregnated with cleanser; dirty nappy holder with lid; changing mat; changing bag; nappy disposal bags

Baby bath; top-and-tail bowl; cotton wool balls; baby soap, shampoo, flannel and hooded baby towels; baby lotion; brush and comb; nail clippers

Clothes: 4-6 stretch suits; 4-6 vests that fasten between the legs; sun hat; 3 cardigans; 3 pairs of socks; 1 pair bootees; mittens; 1-2 woollen shawls; all-in-one padded suit for going outdoors

Toys (e.g. teddy, mobile)

3-6 months

Full-sized cot (new design travel cots can double as a play-pen); new mattress and bedding: at least 4 cotton sheets, 4 cellular blankets and 1 thicker blanket

Buggy: if you are an outdoor family, consider the three-wheeled all-terrain buggies now available

High chair with safety harness

Plastic weaning spoons

Plastic weaning bowls with hot water compartment to keep food warm

Plastic weaning beaker with no-spill spout

Plastic, easy-clean, re-usable bib or 4 washable bibs

Follow-on infant formula if not breast-feeding

Baby rice and cereals for weaning from around 4-6 months onwards

Purée equipment

Bottles of puréed baby food for convenience when necessary

Disposable nappies plus wipes and creams as before

Larger sized clothes as before

Educational toys: rattles; activity centres; sturdy books

Consider door-frame bouncer

6-12 months

Play pen (or travel cot which can double as one)

Stage 2 car seat if previously using an infant carrier

Infant formula

Plastic two-handed weaning cup

Larger bottles of weaning food with lumps (from 7 months)

Larger sized clothes as before in wider selection of styles

Educational toys appropriate for this age-group

Safety cupboard locks; window locks; stair gates; fireguards; fridge locks, socket covers etc.

We had a boy first, then a girl. This was useful from a cost point of view as I didn't mind putting our little girl into blue clothes. I would have felt uncomfortable if it was the other way round however – I couldn't have let my little boy wear pink!
Sharne

If you are expecting twins, your costs will be almost double those estimated for equipping one child. You will need twice the amount of most items (e.g. cots, clothes, nappies, food) although you will also find that people also tend to be more generous with donating items they no longer use.

Having a second baby is obviously much cheaper as you will already have a collection of essential items. You will still need to buy a new cot mattress however and possibly a second baby seat if your other child is still using theirs.

In addition to the money needed to equip a new baby, one of the greatest effects on a family's income is the loss, or partial loss, of one parent's income, either during maternity leave (see chapter 7 for information on legal rights to Statutory Maternity Pay) or during the pre-school years when about a third of mothers opt to stay at home. An individual earning £15,000 per annum who has taken the minimum statutory maternity leave of 18 weeks will sustain an income loss of £2,600. If the full statutory entitlement to maternity leave is taken, however, this can amount to a loss of income of £9,500 over the maternity period.

I had intended returning to work early from maternity leave as we needed the money. By the time we took tax and the cost of childcare into account however, the gain was less than we thought. I therefore decided to stay off for almost a year to enjoy my new baby. Kate

We pay our child allowance into a National Savings Account for our son. By the time he leaves school he will have several thousand pounds saved up. All his Christmas and birthday money goes in, too. Richard

Childcare

The childcare market is predominantly unregulated and remains so despite the government's pledge to introduce safe, affordable nursery education centres. Many parents are forced to rely on ad hoc care such as friends and family and many more are forced to use more than one sort of childcare.

A number of options are available to working mothers, which vary dramatically in terms of cost and flexibility. More and more women are returning to work after childbirth – surveys show that two thirds (67 percent) of new mothers returned to work in 1997, compared with less than half (47 percent) in 1987. With childcare costs in the UK the highest in Europe and no tax concessions to meet this high cost, many mothers find themselves spending a large part of their salary on childcare provision (on average 50 percent). Costs vary from area to area, but generally speaking a family could expect to pay between £70 and £180 a week for a nursery, £50 and 120 for a childminder and £100 and 300 for a nanny. Typically, a family with two children can expect to pay a minimum of £6,000 per annum for childcare.

The concept of Early-Year Centres (Government-funded childcare centres) became a reality at the end of 1997, offering parents affordable and reliable childcare both before and after school. The Government has also pledged to create 30,000 additional after-school clubs to provide out-of-school care for approximately one million schoolchildren with working parents.

Every mother is also entitled to Child Benefit which can be paid weekly or monthly either by cheque or directly into a bank account.

Financial planning

The capital expenditure along with losing a salary, even temporarily, can cause a severe dent in the family's finances. In those families who choose to educate their children privately the effect on the family's finances can be even greater. Combine this with a decision to opt for private medical and dental care, together with the general costs of housing and running the home, then the matter of future financial planning becomes extremely important.

Mortgages
Many different mortgage options are now available, and these

should be carefully considered when thinking about having a baby. It is sometimes worth changing to a different scheme, or even a different mortgage provider. Most banks and building societies offer variable rate mortgages allowing payments to be suspended for up to six months, for example, but although this may have certain attractions, it will usually involve an initial financial penalty. Fixed-rate mortgages can be a good idea for those planning to have a family – simply knowing what your costs are going to be is invaluable. It is advisable to 'shop around' and to seek professional advice before choosing a new mortgage or switching from your current scheme.

State education

State education does not come entirely free. On average, families spend at least £700 annually on getting a child ready for the start of the school year (on uniforms, shoes, gym equipment, stationery, satchels and so on), and a further £120 for additional supplies during the following 12 months. Additional money may also be spent on special outings such as school trips. Multiply that by two children, and for each school year, and the figure becomes quite significant.

Private education

Private school fees range from £600 to £1,100 a term for pre-preparatory three- to seven-year-olds; from £950 to £3,500 for prep schools and from £1,300 to £4,600 for senior schools. You will need to set aside a minimum of £40,000 to educate a day pupil up to the age of 16 – and three times that if you select a boarding school.

Saving

Many saving options can help you finance your child's education, and it is a good idea to find a good independent financial advisor who can provide details and advice on all the available schemes. Many parents pay school fees through a combination of income and savings and the earlier the saving starts, the less will have to be found from salaries at the time. Investing money for education is much the same as investing for anything but the key to education investments must be their flexibility as parents need to draw capital regularly at the beginning of each term. Consider the following:

- High paying deposit accounts, which provide a safe haven for

Education is the best gift you can give your child. We decided to pay for our son to have a first-class private education until the age of eleven, then we will reassess the situation according to his needs and the best school to suit him. If necessary, we will continue to go the private route. Anya

I took out two savings plans eight years ago, when I was single, in which I saved £50 per month each in investment trusts. These mature in two years. While I had initially ear-marked them to buy a sports car, they are just right for paying for our toddler's education.
Sarah

funds, particularly if parents are less than five years away from paying fees.

- National Savings and Tess, which also provide safe homes for savings as will the new Individual Saving Accounts (ISAs). Although Tessas will not be available from April 1999, individuals will not lose the tax benefits that previously applied.

If parents are planning for the longer term it may be advisable to use collective investments such as unit trusts and investment trusts.

- Personal Equity Plans (PEPs) are one of the most efficient ways to invest and allow funds to be withdrawn when needed as returns are tax free. PEPs, like Tessas, will not be available from April 1999, but individuals will not lose the tax benefits that previously applied.
- Endowment policies offer an attractive way of saving if parents have time to take out longer-term policies. Their lack of flexibility may be a drawback, particularly if policy holders need to surrender early – they may find the policy is of little value. There are two types of endowment policy: a unit-linked policy which rises and falls with the stock market; and a with profits policy which guarantees a minimum payout to which a bonus is added each year. Endowment policies are always for fixed terms and often include life assurance so that children will still be provided for in the event of a parent's death.

There are a number of other ways to invest for education, including specialist school fee plans, Friendly Society schemes, and life assurance. One of the most popular uses of life assurance, for example, is to use a charitable trust to invest a lump sum which offers a guaranteed way of paying fees on a term basis.

Further education
Many children no longer qualify for more than a nominal grant to assist their further education. Parents may therefore need to continue saving plans until their children leave higher education at around the age of 21. Although it is not yet completely clear how student finances will operate in the future, and whether or not the full costs of tuition fees will have to be met by individuals, it is likely that the cost of higher education will soar and students and their families will have to pay a higher share of that increased cost.

Life insurance

Many investments do not include life insurance and parents may wish to arrange life cover separately. The cost of this varies, depending upon age, occupation and health. Identifying the level and type of cover to take out will depend on individuals' circumstances, but those with young families are usually advised to have life cover worth at least ten times their annual income.

There are many forms of life cover, including term assurance which pays out a lump sum in the event of death of the policyholder over a given period of time. The policyholder can increase the sum assured automatically (at a revised premium) to take an expanding family and education costs into account.

- A couple in their late twenties (neither of whom smoke) could expect to pay a monthly premium of approximately £12.00 for the male and £9.00 for the female and this would provide term assurance of £100,000 for 20 years.
- Joint life policies offer couples another option which pays out should one of them die during the specified period. For example a couple in their late twenties who are starting a family could expect to pay a monthly premium of approximately £15.00 for a joint term assurance of £80,000 for 20 years to cover their children's early years. Some policies offer a replacement income for the policyholder's family for a set number of years, providing a period of stability for the remaining parent and children.

Health and dental insurance

The National Health Service still provides excellent health and dental care, but many families prefer to have the option of private health and dental care in conjunction with the services offered by the NHS.

Over 30 organizations in the UK currently offer private health insurance cover with fairly broad differentials in cost and provision of service. Your choice of a private medical insurance plan should not be based on cost alone as there are restrictions and limitations on medical insurance cover particularly on the less expensive plans. Ask an independent financial advisor who specializes in private medical and dental insurance to help you before deciding which policy to adopt.

An average family (two adults aged 35 with two children aged two

We pay a small amount per month towards a private dental plan. There didn't seem to be any NHS dentists in our area who were taking on new patients. I believe the local authority is obliged to provide NHS dental treatment if we request it, but we would have to travel a fair distance, so we opted for the surgery down the road.
Mick

and three) can expect to pay around £1,000 a year for the lower 'C' band medical cover, with one of the leading insurers. Premiums increase as parents and dependants get older however, so that by the time parents are 50 and the children 16 and 17, they can expect to pay approximately £1,600 per annum.

Free NHS dental care is available for children up to the age of 18, and for women who are pregnant (and up to a year after the birth of their child). Some children may require orthodontic care which is not covered by the NHS. Parents are advised to set aside £2,000 per child (per lifetime) should this type of dentistry be required.

A number of different schemes provide private dental care, with costs varying widely depending on restrictions in the provision of service. An average family (two adults and two children) can expect to pay approximately £400 per annum. Other insurers offer weekly premiums of, for example, £12 which provides £240-worth of dental care per annum for each member of the family. Beware, though – insurers often disallow orthodontic work, and there are ceilings on certain benefits such as the amount of routine work that can be carried out in a single year.

A number of companies also offer budget plans with monthly payments based on the dentist's estimation of an individual's annual dentistry bill.

Insurance for multiple birth

Only a small number of firms are prepared to insure against multiple births and provide benefits should this event occur. A number of years ago, before the advent of sophisticated scanning techniques, it was more readily available. Today there are stringent checks at the time of taking out the insurance, parents need to prove that they have not yet had a scan for example.

There are two types of insurance: the first can be taken out during pregnancy but before the mother reaches the eleventh week (and has not yet had a scan); the second can be taken out over a two-year period during which time the woman must conceive and give birth.

The cost of insuring a 30-year-old woman with no history of twins in the family would be £41 per £1,000 insured up to a maximum of £3,000. This figure can go as high as £80 per £1,000 depending on family history.

Financial implications of being married or unmarried

Tax
In addition to the single person's allowance, married couples enjoy an extra tax allowance each year. Additional relief, in respect of children, can be claimed by single parents or a separated spouse, which equals a married couple's additional allowance. The married person's allowance cannot be claimed by those co-habiting in any circumstances whatsoever, so from a tax point of view there are advantages to being married before having children. Furthermore, transferring assets is more easily done between those who are married than those who are not.

Property
With regard to property, an unmarried couple's home should be held in both their names (a joint tenancy), especially if they plan to have a baby. This ensures that should either one of them die, the other automatically inherits the home. Many couples who share a home do so under a 'tenancy in common' where each couple owns 50 percent of the property. When one of them dies, however, the surviving partner does not necessarily inherit his or her partner's share of the house. It is therefore very important for individuals to have made a will (see below).

Pensions
The law regarding pensions is currently under review. At present, if a man should die while drawing his pension, his wife may be entitled to a proportion of that pension, depending on the type of pension, but this is not the case where a couple are unmarried. If the man dies before he draws his pension, either the value of the pension fund would go into his estate (of which his wife would be the beneficiary) or his spouse may entitled to a proportion of the prospective pension. Many private pensions make provision for dependant children, often paying out a quarter of the spouse's pension for each child. This would not automatically be the case with unmarried couples.

Wills
Seventy percent of people fail to make a will, and dying intestate (i.e.

without making a will) can financially prejudice the surviving spouse/partner. (For more information, see chapter 7.)

Setting up trust funds and covenants

Parents and grandparents might consider setting up a trust fund to:

- provide additional income for their grandchildren's future
- avoid paying inheritance tax
- fund their grandchildren's education.

Many products are specifically labelled as investment schemes for children. Investment trusts enable the risk to be spread, while giving good long-term potential for growth and allowing families to match their investment needs to the right type of trust. Some investment trusts concentrate on long-term capital growth while others offer high or increasing income, or a balance of income and capital growth.

With regard to holding shares, children are not allowed to exercise voting rights or to sign documents transferring title. A parent must therefore become the registered owner of the shares, with the child as the beneficial owner.

- More formal agreements can be set up, specifying the trustees and other relevant details. Alternatively a formal bare trust document can be drawn up with a solicitor. The adult, who is the trustee (this can be a parent or godparent or friend), looks after the investment on behalf of the child until they are 18.

- More complicated trusts can specify particular wishes, for example allowing a child to receive income from the trust only from the age of 18, and access to the capital at the age of 30. Specific restrictions to the trust may have tax implications and it is therefore advisable to seek expert advice before setting up a trust.

Children's personal tax allowance

Children, like everyone else, have a personal tax allowance, and income from investments set up by grandparents or friends is taxed as the child's. Providing it does not exceed the allowance, this will be exempt from tax. Should a parent give money to his/her own child and they receive income of more than £100 a year from that gift however, the income will be added to the parents' taxable income. An individual is allowed to give up to £3,000 out of their income tax-free annually.

The first £223,000 (1998/99) of an individual's assets is free of inheritance tax. After that tax is paid at the rate of 40 percent. The beneficiaries of a trust can receive the income or it can be allowed to accumulate, and the assets are exempt from inheritance tax if the donor lives for seven years after making the transfer. However if the donor were to die in the first three years after making the gift or transferring it to the trust, the tax has to be paid in full. The tax due is reduced by 20 percent in the fourth year, 40 percent in the fifth, 60 percent in the sixth and 80 percent in the seventh, and only after seven years is the gift exempt from tax. This is a complex area and again, it is advisable to seek professional advice.

Children also have the same annual capital gains tax threshold as adults. If, after capital losses, their total capital gains exceed this threshold, they will be liable for capital gains tax.

Until the mid-to-late 1990s, children were entitled to tax relief on the money paid by parents or grandparents by way of a Deed of Covenant, but this benefit has since been abolished and is therefore no longer an attractive way of investing capital.

When my godchildren were born, I started a children's investment trust for each of them. I pay in money at Christmas and on birthdays and the sum has already more than doubled in just a few years. The fund also sends me a birthday card to send on to the child, which ensures I don't forget! Gemma

Chapter 7:

Legal Implications of

Having a Baby[3]

by **Siobhan Carolan**

Your first legal requirement as a parent is to register your baby's birth. This should be done within six weeks of the event and is just one of many legal requirements arising from being a parent (as well as additional legal rights) that many of us may never before have considered. This chapter looks at pregnancy and parenthood from a legal point of view and can be divided as follows:

- your rights at work
- your legal responsibilities to your child
- legal implications of being married/unmarried/divorced
- making a will
- legal considerations regarding adoption, surrogacy and fostering.

Your rights at work

The government's White Paper, 'Fairness at Work', aims to improve rights for employees and introduce more family-friendly policies. Men and women with more than one year's service will both be allowed a guaranteed three-month parental leave when they have a baby or adopt a child and will be protected against dismissal should they choose to exercise this right. They will also have the right to reasonable time off work for family emergencies, such as a child's illness, regardless of how long they have been in their job.

Maternity leave

There are a number of statutory rights regarding maternity leave, and provided an employee gives proper notification to her employer (written notification at least 21 days before she intends to start

---

3 All figures are correct at time of going to press

taking maternity leave) she is entitled to these whether she works full-time or part-time (see also chapter 4). Her rights fall into four main categories:

- **Time off for antenatal care:** pregnant workers should not be unreasonably refused time away from work for antenatal care and this time off should be paid for at the employee's normal rate of pay. Antenatal care covers medical examinations and also related classes such as parentcraft. These rights apply irrespective of length of service.

- **Protection against unfair dismissal on maternity-related grounds:** it is unlawful to either dismiss or make an employee redundant simply because she is pregnant, or because she is on statutory maternity leave. This protection can extend for up to four weeks after the end of the worker's statutory maternity leave if, due to ill health, she has been unable to return to work as long as she provides a medical certificate. These rights apply irrespective of length of service.

- **Maternity leave and maternity absence:** all pregnant workers (irrespective of length of service) are entitled to 14 weeks' statutory maternity leave. The Government White Paper 'Fairness at Work' proposes to extend this to 18 weeks which will bring it in line with maternity pay. An employee must continue to receive all her contractual benefits, such as private medical cover, or company car, during the statutory maternity leave period.

Those workers who have been employed continuously for more than two years are entitled to an additional period of maternity absence, lasting from the end of their maternity leave up to the end of the 28th week after the week in which their baby is born. If an employee decides to take this additional leave, she must notify her employer. It is then a matter for agreement between her and her employer whether she continues to receive her contractual benefits as discussed above.

- **Maternity benefits:** pregnant employees are entitled to receive up to 18 weeks of statutory maternity pay (SMP) from their employers, provided they have worked for their employer for a continuous period of 26 weeks ending with the qualifying week (i.e. the fifteenth week before the due date) and as long as they earn a certain minimum weekly wage in the eight weeks up to

I was made redundant while on maternity leave. My employer claimed there were no alternative jobs suitable for me but when I sought legal advice, they agreed to pay me compensation. I'm not confrontational by nature but having a young baby to support made me fight tooth and nail for my rights.

Anne

(and including) the qualifying week.

SMP is paid irrespective of whether or not an employee intends to return to work. The rate of SMP is usually 90 percent of the employee's salary for the first six weeks and a set, nominal sum thereafter.

Women who are not entitled to SMP, but meet the qualifying position based on their recent National Insurance record (for example those who are self-employed), are entitled to claim a nominal maternity allowance (MA). MA is also payable to women who are unemployed from the eleventh week before the due date. MA is paid by the Benefits Agency for up to 18 weeks. Women who are not employed or who are self-employed in the qualifying week are entitled to a slightly reduced MA.

Returning to work

An employee does not have to notify her employer of her return to work if she intends to return after the end of the statutory maternity leave period. If she wishes to return before the end of the leave period however, she must give seven days' written notice of her date of return.

Employees who have taken advantage of additional maternity leave must give their employers 21 days' written notice of her date of return. An employer is also entitled to write to those on additional maternity leave asking them in advance (no earlier than 21 days before the end of statutory maternity period) if they still intend to return to work.

Should an employee be unable to return to work at the end of either the 14-week period or 28 week period due to ill health she is entitled to a further four weeks' absence provided she can produce a medical certificate in advance. The employer may also postpone the employee's date of return by up to four weeks provided she is notified in advance of the reasons for the postponement.

Once an employee returns to work, whether she has been on statutory maternity leave or additional maternity absence, she is entitled to the same job and the same terms and conditions of work as before. These may only be varied by mutual agreement. Should redundancy arise during an employee's maternity leave or on her return to work, she must be offered a role/grade equivalent to that of the redundant position.

Employers and employees are, of course, free to agree longer periods of leave entitlement on a voluntary or contractual basis.

Your legal responsibilities to your child

Although parental responsibility, under the 1989 Children's Act, means all the legal rights, duties and responsibilities of a parent in relation to a child (and his property), it does not set out what exactly these rights and responsibilities are. To determine what is meant by them, reference to previous cases would be needed. Apart from any legal obligation, the moral duty of a parent to maintain, care for and control a child, and to provide education, has been recognized in previous cases and although in common law there is no legal obligation to provide for a child, by statute it is an offence to neglect, abandon, assault or maltreat a child or to allow others to do so.

Since 1993 parents have been legally obliged to provide for their child, and in the case of an absent father, even though he may not have parental responsibility, he is still legally required to provide maintenance for any child under the age of 16 or under the age of 19 and in full-time education (excluding further education i.e. university).

The belief today is that parental responsibilities exist only so long as they are required for the protection of the child (and his property). It is no longer accepted that children remain under parental control until a specified age. Parental responsibility cease when a child reaches an age when he/she is able to demonstrate sufficient understanding of a situation to enable him/her to make their own decision.

A parent is not liable for a crime committed by their child. However, parents can be ordered to pay the fines arising from compensation orders in juvenile proceedings.

Appointing a guardian

Before appointing a guardian for your infant children, it is important to consider the concept of 'parental responsibility' as defined in the 1989 Children's Act. It is often believed that both parents of a child have parental responsibility but this is not true in all cases. If the parents were married at the time of the child's birth, or if a child has been adopted by a couple, both parents have parental responsibility. In any other case in which the law treats a child as being the legitimate child of a couple both parents have parental responsibility.

When my brother's children were born, he asked me to act as guardian should he and his wife die. Now we have had our own child, we have named him in turn to look after our daughter should the need arise. It makes me feel more comfortable when travelling with my work to know she will be well loved and cared for should anything happen to me. Deirdre

In all other cases, however, it is only the mother that has parental responsibility – even if a couple have lived together for a number of years and decide to have children. The father does not have parental responsibility unless he has acquired it by a formal agreement with the mother (see 'The legal implications of being married/unmarried /divorced' below) or by a court order. Parents without parental responsibility may not appoint guardians.

The function of a guardian is to take over the parental responsibility of the child after the parent's death. Where both parents have parental responsibility, the guardianship can only take effect when both parents die. The only exceptions are if at the time of the appointing parent's death, he/she was the only parent in whose favour there was a residence order under the 1989 Act or that he/she was the only parent with care and control of the child through a care and control order made under previous legislation.

Where one parent dies and the other parent did not have parental responsibility, the guardianship would come into force even if the other parent were still alive. It is important to note the following:

- The consent of whomever a parent wishes to appoint as guardian must be obtained and normally they are appointed by the parents' will.

- Financial provision for the cost of feeding, clothing, educating and generally looking after the child is usually paid out of the parent's estate so that the guardian should not be out of pocket. Parents often leave what is called a 'letter of wishes' asking the trustees of the will to exercise their powers to ensure that this is achieved.

- A parent can always revoke an earlier choice and appoint a new guardian so long as it is documented in a new will.

- Once a guardian has been appointed he or she has the right to appoint a guardian to act in the event of his or her own death.

- The court has the power, at the request of the child and in other circumstances, to bring a guardian's appointment to an end.

Legal implications of being married/unmarried/divorced
English law continues to make definite distinctions between couples who are married and those who are unmarried, and is more stringent where marriage is concerned. For example, a refusal of sex, or unfaithfulness, may give rise to matrimonial proceedings whereas

cohabitees have no such right. However, as it has become more socially acceptable to cohabit and to have children out of wedlock – women born since 1960 are twice as likely to live with a partner without marrying than were the previous generation, and one in 12 will have a baby out of wedlock – the legal recognition of cohabitation has grown. Unfortunately, parents who cohabit are four times more likely to split up than those who are married which means that half of unmarried couples with children separate within ten years compared with only one in eight couples with children who are married.

Property

Marriage gives couples the legal right to equal shares of property and other assets, co-habitation gives no such automatic rights. Although historically, in divorce cases, spouses could rely upon the court dealing with such matters equitably, in recent years cohabitees are enjoying more favourable treatment than they have previously received.

There are no rights for a cohabitee if their partner dies intestate (i.e. without making a will) under the Administration of Estates Act 1925. There are different rights for cohabitees from those of a wife under the Inheritance Act 1975 (i.e. only if they are dependent), but the same rights under the Pneumoconiosis (Workers' Compensation Act) 1979. Making a will is discussed in more detail below, but it cannot be stressed too strongly how important it is for both partners to make a will, whether married or cohabiting.

Financial support for children

It is required by the Child Support Act 1991 and the 1989 Children's Act that parents, whether they cohabit, or are married or live separately, be legally responsible for the financial support of their children. It is only in the eventuality of divorce that the financial and other arrangements made for the children of a marriage become open to greater scrutiny by the courts.

'Parental responsibility'

The greatest and most significant difference between couples who are married and those who are not from a legal point of view concerns their parental responsibility: under the 1989 Children's Act, married parents are each automatically granted 'parental

Paul and I got married when I was eight months pregnant as we discovered that should the baby be illegitimate, Paul would have no legal parental rights. Even though we were in a long-term stable relationship, this seemed terribly unfair all round. Susan

responsibility', whereas in the case of unmarried couples only the mother is granted it, irrespective of whether or not the couple are in a stable relationship.

The father can acquire parental responsibility by agreement with his partner. This is called a Parental Responsibility Agreement and must be filed in the Principal Registry of the Family Division. The advantage of this type of agreement is that it does not involve recourse to the courts. This agreement puts the unmarried father in the same position as the married father.

If two partners are not living together and an agreement is difficult to reach, the father can apply for a Parental Responsibility Order. This will only be granted, however, if the court believes it to be in the best interest of the child – the child's welfare is the primary consideration. The father can also apply for a contact order, or even a residence order, to allow him to see the child or indeed have the child live with him.

Separation/divorce

The legal view is that when a marriage ends it should be the end of the spousal relationship only and not the end of the parents' relationship with their children. One of the most significant factors in a child's recovery following divorce is the quality of the arrangements for seeing both parents. Sadly, it is estimated that 50 percent of divorced and separated fathers lose contact with their children within two years. The 1989 Children's Act allows more flexibility for parents to reach their own agreements regarding the arrangement for their children and encourages the continuation of the parent-child relationship.

The Family Law Act 1996 requires couples to be aware of mediation sessions – these offer an opportunity for couples to reach joint, amicable decisions on contentious issues such as access to children, financial support, division of assets and housing. Before this and the 1989 Children's Act, there was little to encourage joint responsibility or to preserve an ongoing relationship between parents and children. The law now encourages continued parental involvement in cases of separation and divorce and the concept of parental responsibility supports this view.

The following points regarding parents' roles following separation/divorce are worth noting:

- Parental responsibility for children remains with both parents whether they are divorced or separated. Either parent can implement parental responsibility when the child is with them and each parent can act independently with regard to their responsibility.
- If one parent is unhappy or objects to what the other is doing then an application must be made to court. One of the main thrusts of the 1989 Children's Act is to ensure that the parent-child relationship continues and to this end the absent parent has the right to be completely involved and have their say in the child's upbringing.
- The 1989 Children's Act favours a policy of non-intervention, meaning that intervention by the courts is only justified when it is in the best interests of the child. Parents are left to make their own financial and domestic arrangements whenever possible. An order would only be made in cases of real dispute, or where a practical problem (e.g. housing) arises.

In divorce proceedings examination of arrangements is done through completion of what is called a D8A (statement of arrangements for children) which sets out the parents' proposals regarding their children. Essentially the court will want to know where they will live; with whom; whether the other parent will see them and how frequently; arrangements for their day-to-day care; information about their health; where they will attend school; and what financial support has been provided. A hearing will only take place if something in the paperwork seems amiss.

The two main orders under the 1989 Children's Act reflect these issues and this is the area where parents may need the most help in resolving problems but the emphasis again is upon the parent-child relationship. The orders provide answers to questions on a practical level in relation to a child's upbringing.

The 1989 Children's Act is also concerned with the principle of delay in recognition of the anxiety a child may feel while they wait for the outcome of divorce proceedings.

The welfare checklist is only used in cases under dispute and it clearly puts the child's welfare and interests first. When parents are in full agreement with regard to any children, however, the welfare checklist would not apply.

The 1989 Children's Act allows the children themselves to make

We changed our will once we decided to start a family, to include any future children. We were spurred into it when we read about a local couple who were killed and left a small child – both sets of grandparents were fighting for custody. We wanted to specify who would be guardians ourselves. Jo

an application to court so long as they can prove they have sufficient understanding of the issues in question.

Parents are required by both the Child Support Act 1991 and the 1989 Children's Act to be legally responsible for the financial support of their children. The Child Support Agency can act on behalf of those on State benefits to enforce an absent parent to make maintenance payments

Making a will

There is no legal obligation to make a will, but it is a good idea to do so if you intend to have a baby. If you die without making a will, you are said to have died intestate and your property/assets will be divided among your family according to legal regulations: your spouse will be entitled to receive all your personal chattels, a fixed sum of £125,000 (if there is that much), with a life interest in half the residue, with children and grandchildren sharing the other half. (In the case of cohabitees, when one partner dies without making a will, the surviving partner will only be entitled to assets held jointly.)

Making a will is strongly advised, particularly where children are involved or in the case of unmarried couples because:

- it ensures that your assets go to the people you choose
- it allows you to choose your own executors
- the business of administering your estate is made more efficient
- it can give executors and trustees wider powers of investment and advancement of funds than the law normally allows
- if you have many assets it may be possible to pay less tax if you leave a properly drawn up will.

If a will is in any way complicated then it is advisable to seek the advice of a solicitor. In straightforward cases, as long as individuals clearly state their wishes and sign at the end of the will, with two witnesses to their signature, their will is valid. The will should detail the appointment of guardians for children (see above) in the event of the deaths of both parents.

Executors

The choosing and appointing of executors is extremely important – it is a responsible position and on occasion there may be a lot of work involved. You can name up to four executors altogether and it is usual for a husband to name his wife and vice versa as well as a professional such as a solicitor or a bank, although this will involve a fee.

Division of property

The most important part of the will is the section stating how property is to be divided. Most people leave their property to their immediate family. If you fail to provide for your wife, husband, children or anyone else financially dependent upon you, they are entitled to apply to the courts for reasonable provision to be made for them out of the estate, under the Inheritance (Provision for Family and Dependants) Act, 1975.

Any alterations to wills are made by adding what is called a 'codicil' and this has to be signed and witnessed like a will. If there are a number of alterations, it is advisable to write out a new will with a clause revoking the old one.

If an individual makes a will and then marries, the law states that the will is no longer valid and a new one should be drawn up. If a will is made while married, but an individual subsequently divorces, not all the provisions of the will are automatically revoked and it is therefore advisable to make a new will. It is equally important to update wills if financial circumstances change, particularly if this could have implications with regard to inheritance tax.

Legal considerations regarding adoption, surrogacy and fostering

Adoption

The main law governing adoption is the Adoption Act 1976 but the 1989 Children's Act has made many changes designed to improve on this.

Under the Adoption Act, 1976, if the adopters are married, their adopted child is treated in law as if he/she had been born a child of the marriage. Where the adopting parent is single, the adopted child is treated as if he/she had been born to the adopter in wedlock (but not as a child of any actual marriage of the adopter) – in other words the adopted child is not considered illegitimate.

There is a huge amount of administration surrounding adoption, and many issues need to be considered, including:

- the role of adoption agencies, local authorities
- social workers' reports

I made my first will just after I separated from my first husband. I didn't realize it became invalid when I married again. My husband and I have now drawn up reciprocal wills leaving everything to each other or, if we should both die, to our child. It was awful having to consider what to do should he die with us – but you have to face these possibilities in advance if you don't want both sides of the family in dispute.
Bridget

- the ages of prospective parents
- the length of time the child must spend with the prospective parents before the court hearing
- parental responsibility of adoptive parents
- prospective parents can be married or single but an unmarried couple may not jointly adopt.

Those wishing to adopt must apply to their local social services department and obtain a list of adoption agencies (see chapter 13). These act largely autonomously, there are no national guidelines relating to the personal suitability of applicants and there have been criticisms in the past of adoption agencies and their reliance on ideology and dogma. The overall aim of adoption is to promote the welfare of the child throughout his/her childhood. Every local authority is legally required to provide an adoption service.

By law, adoption agencies must:

- provide counselling services to find out if prospective parents are suitable
- explain any legal procedures and implications
- set up case records and obtain written reports by a medical practitioner regarding the health of prospective parents
- provide reports on applicants' premises and the suitability of their home
- obtain written reports of interview with referees.

Once all this has been done, they must prepare a written report to present to the Adoption Panel or another Adoption Agency.

The court's decision is based upon the need to safeguard and promote the welfare of the child throughout his childhood and in addition, where applicable, a child's wishes will be taken into consideration before a decision is made.

Once a child has been legally adopted, he/she will receive a new birth certificate showing the names of the adopted parents. At the age of 18 the adopted child has the right to trace his/her birth parents (no such right exists for the birth parents themselves). An Adoption Contact Register is available at the Registrar of Births, Marriage and Deaths, where both parents and children can register their details.

Anybody wishing to adopt a child from abroad must prepare themselves for a long and drawn-out process. The 1993 White Paper 'Adoption: The Future' suggests that it should be a criminal offence to bring a child into the UK without permission from the relevant authorities. Local authorities are now required to help individuals seeking an overseas adoption however, and will prepare a report on the suitability of prospective applicants for the Department of Health. Prospective parents will also need to contact the Home Office Immigration and Nationality Department for information about procedures.

Surrogacy

As the technology surrounding assisted fertility becomes more sophisticated, a number of moral, ethical and legal issues are raised. The Human Fertilization and Embryology Act 1990 provides the legal framework surrounding the issues of surrogacy, IVF and artificial insemination.

A surrogate mother is a woman who bears a child at the request of another person, with a view to that person becoming the child's parent. No surrogacy arrangement is enforceable by law, by or against those making it. In addition, surrogate motherhood is not against the law, but paying for another woman to have a child for you, save paying her expenses, is. By law, the birth mother of a surrogate child is the legal mother and therefore it would be necessary for the commissioning parents to adopt the child and take on the parental responsibility.

Surrogacy is an extremely complex area and it is therefore best to seek professional legal advice about the relative rights of the genetic and host parents if you are contemplating such arrangements.

Fostering

It is the duty of a local authority to provide accommodation and maintenance for a child in its care and this can be done by placing the child with a family who are described as local authority foster parents.

Foster parents are generally approved by local authorities following stringent checks and interviews with two referees. There is an examination of the 'foster home' to check its suitability and other members of the 'foster family' are also checked out.

By law there must always be a Foster Care Agreement between the foster parent and local authority covering:

- foster parents caring for the child as if they were a member of the family

- procedures for review of a foster parent
- foster placement agreements (see below)
- the amount of support and training provided to foster parents
- confidentiality.

A child cannot be placed with a foster parent until there is a written agreement called a Foster Placement Agreement. This covers, among other things:

- a child's personal history
- religious and cultural background
- health and education needs
- the authority's arrangements for financial support; and contact with the child's parents.

Once a foster parent has been approved they are reviewed annually. The local authority are obliged to visit foster homes from time to time and in particular during the first year. If they are not satisfied with what they see they will terminate the approval.

Gay parenting: Parental responsibility
by **Lisa Saffron**

The law is used to legitimize family bonds that are not based on biological ties. Legal bonds are created by marriage, child support and adoption laws, are dissolved by divorce laws and are reinforced by laws and rulings covering inheritance, insurance, state benefits, immigration, housing and many other aspects of life. Unfortunately, most family law does not accept the social bonds created by lesbians and gay men.

The legal implications of limiting marriage to heterosexual couples is that lesbian or gay couples cannot achieve the same recognition of their families and of the role of the non-birth mother. The 1989 Children's Act sets out who is entitled to legally recognized parenthood. It defines parental responsibility as 'all the rights, duties, powers and responsibilities and authority which by law a parent of a child has in relation to the child and his property.' The birth mother, whether married or not, automatically has parental responsibility. So does a married father. An unmarried father does not but can acquire parental responsibility by making an agreement with the birth mother (which must be witnessed and registered with the court) or by applying to court for a parental responsibility order. In the eyes of the law a sperm donor, whether anonymous or known, is an unmarried father.

Although not intended by the lawmakers, the 1989 Children's Act makes it possible for a lesbian co-parent to apply for a joint residence order which effectively gives her parental responsibility. With a residence order, a co-parent could consent to medical treatment and school outings. But as long as they are co-parenting amicably, possession of the residence order has little practical effect on their day-to-day life. Its real importance is as a symbol of legal recognition of the lesbian partner's role as a parent and as a safeguard for her if the birth mother were to try to cut her out of the family.

Margaret says:

We have decided to apply for a joint residence order so that my partner, Cecilia, has parental responsibility for our 17-month-old daughter Leah. I've written a will naming Cecilia as Leah's guardian. If anything happens to me, I want Leah to remain with Cecilia. The residence order would acknowledge Cecilia's role as Leah's parent and be an extra safeguard in case my parents try to take Leah to live with them. I have a difficult relationship with my parents and don't want them to have Leah. It's too painful to think about what would happen if Cecilia and I split up. I don't know that I would want Leah to be divided equally between us. But I can't think about that now.

Karen, in a lesbian relationship with Traci, on trying to get pregnant:

Both my partner and the donor will apply for parental responsibility right after the birth. He doesn't get that automatically because we're not married. It makes sense for him to have that too. We expect that the child will go and stay with him by itself when it's old enough. If the donor has to make decisions and sign consents, or if anything happens while the child is with him, he'll need to have parental responsibility.

Chapter 8:
Your Health Before You Conceive

The advantage of planning well in advance to have a baby is that both the potential mother and father can follow a full preconceptual care programme. This helps to ensure that both you and your partner are in the peak of health before trying to conceive, and will maximize the chances of a successful outcome.

Preconceptual care is important, as one of the most critical times of a baby's development is the first four weeks of gestation – often before the mother is even aware she is pregnant. Studies suggest that if a baby is undernourished at this critical time, it may become programmed to develop conditions such as high blood pressure, coronary heart disease, stroke and diabetes in later life. It is never too soon to adopt a healthy diet and lifestyle where pregnancy and your future offspring are concerned. You should start preparing your body for pregnancy at least three months (preferably six or more) before conception. In fact, if there is even a chance that you might decide to have a baby within the next year or two, the time to start a preconceptual care programme is now.

Preconceptual care is just as important for the future father as it is for the mother. It takes around a 100 days to produce a sperm, from start to finish. That's 100 crucial days in which you can ensure that your sperm are in the peak of health before being called on to do their duty.

This chapter is divided into three sections, with diet and lifestyle advice aimed in particular at future mothers and future fathers, or, more generally, for both.

Advice for future mothers

Early on when you are thinking of having a baby, it is worth having a

My doctor told me I would need to lose weight before trying to have a baby. I went on a low-fat diet and started to walk at least a mile every day. Once I felt fitter, I took up jogging. I have now lost two stone and finally feel ready to think about having that baby. My husband has lost around half a stone too – we are both in this together!
Jo-Anne

well woman/pre-natal check with your doctor to:

- check your blood pressure is normal
- check your urine is clear of albumin (protein) and glucose (sugar)
- ensure your cervical smear test is up-to-date and normal
- see whether you need to change any medications you are taking
- establish whether you need referral to an obstetrician for prenatal advice – especially if you are taking treatments for epilepsy, or have diabetes
- have your antibody levels against rubella (German measles) checked
- ensure you are taking the right dose of folic acid
- see if you need any dietary or weight loss advice.

Weight
If you are thinking about having a baby one day, it is important to try losing as much excess weight as possible, so you fall into the recommended healthy weight range for your height. This will increase the chances of a successful healthy pregnancy and reduce the risk of complications such as gestational diabetes, high blood pressure (pre-eclampsia) and difficult birth. This is especially important if you are apple-shaped and tend to store excess weight around your middle, which has been shown to reduce the chance of conceiving by as much as 30 percent in some overweight women (see next page for a healthy weight for height chart for both men and women).

If you need to lose weight, it is important do so slowly and safely before having a baby. Sudden weight loss and crash dieting may harm the health of both you and your future baby, and lead to a lack of important vitamins and minerals. Aim to lose weight at a rate of no more than 500g-1kg (1-2 pounds) per week, by increasing the amount of exercise you take, and by eating more healthily. Cut out sweet, fatty foods and snacks. Don't cut out dairy products however, as these are an important source of calcium needed for your future baby's developing bones. Switch to low-fat dairy products instead – skimmed and semi-skimmed milk contains just as much calcium as full cream milk, for example, but without the extra fat and calories.

If you are very overweight seek advice from your doctor before embarking on pregnancy.

Underweight women may also have difficulty conceiving compared with those within the normal weight range for their height. They too

Height		Optimum Healthy Weight Range				(Based on body mass index – BMI – 18.7-23.8 for women, and BMI of 20-25 for men)
		Men		Women		
Metres	Feet	Kg	Stones	Kg	Stones	
1.47	4'10"			40-51	6st 4 – 8st	
1.50	4'11"			42-54	6st 8 – 8st 7	
1.52	5ft			43-55	6st 11 – 8st 9	
1.55	5'1"			45-57	7st 1 – 8st 13	
1.57	5'2"			46-59	7st 3 – 9st 4	
1.60	5'3"			48-61	7st 8 – 9st 8	
1.63	5'4"			50-63	7st 12 – 9st 13	
1.65	5'5"			51-65	8st – 10st 3	
1.68	5'6"	56-70	8st 12 – 11st	53-67	8st 5 – 10st 7	
1.70	5'7"	58-72	9st 1 – 11st 4	54-69	8st 7 – 10st 12	
1.73	5'8"	60-75	9st 6 – 11st 10	56-71	8st 11 – 11st 2	
1.75	5'9"	61-76	9st 9 – 12st	57-73	8st 13 – 11st 7	
1.78	5'10"	63-79	9st 13 – 12st 6	59-75	9st 4 – 11st 11	
1.80	5'11"	65-81	10st 3 – 12st 9	61-77	9st 8 – 12st 1	
1.83	6ft	67-83	10st 7 – 13st 1	63-80	9st 13 – 12st 8	
1.85	6'1"	69-85	10st 11 – 13st 5			
1.88	6'2"	71-88	11st 2 – 13st 12			
1.90	6'3"	72-90	11st 5 – 14st 2			
1.93	6'4"	75-93	11st 10 – 14st 8			

The body mass index is calculated on:

$$\frac{\text{weight (kg)}}{\text{height (m) x height (m)}}$$

may need to seek dietary advice. This is especially important for women who have recently suffered from an eating disorder as metabolic changes and long-term lack of nutrients can cause problems with conception and development of the baby if not corrected in time.

Here are some guidelines for your preconceptual diet:

- Eat a healthy, wholefood and varied diet.
- Select organic products to minimize exposure to pesticides, fertilizers, growth enhancers and pollutants.
- Eat at least five portions of well-washed fresh fruit and vegetables per day.
- Increase your intake of foods rich in folic acid as these can help reduce the risk of some developmental defects, including spina bifida. Good dietary sources of folic acid include green leafy vegetables (e.g. spinach, broccoli, Brussels sprouts, kale, spring greens), pulses and foods fortified with folic acid (e.g. some breakfast cereals). Manufacturers have started putting a blue flash on packets to make it easier to select foods fortified with folic acid.
- Increase your intake of essential fatty acids from nuts, seeds and fish, especially oily fish.
- Use olive or rapeseed oil in cooking and for salad dressings.
- Obtain at least half of your daily energy in the form of complex carbohydrates such as wholemeal bread, brown rice, wholegrain cereals, potatoes and wholewheat pasta.
- Drink plenty of fluids, especially mineral or filtered water.
- Use low-fat versions of dairy products and drink an extra pint of semi-skimmed or skimmed milk (preferably organic) per day for calcium.
- Watch the fats in your diet and try not to eat any to excess.
- Avoid convenience, pre-processed foods and additives – eat homemade meals as much as possible.
- Avoid peanuts and peanut (groundnut) oil – especially if there is a family tendency towards allergic conditions.
- Cut back on foods of little nutritional value (e.g. biscuits, cakes, confectionery, pastries).
- Eat regular meals and never skip a meal, especially breakfast.
- Avoid – or limit your intake of – sugar and salt.

- Reduce your intake of caffeinated drinks to no more than three a day.
- Avoid liver and liver products such as pâté or cod liver oil, as they contain high levels of vitamin A which can be harmful during pregnancy (in excess).
- Avoid shellfish, and raw or undercooked eggs because of the risk of Salmonella.
- Avoid unpasteurized and blue cheeses.

Vitamins and minerals

During pregnancy and the preconceptual period, your need for certain vitamins and minerals increases. It is important to take a multinutrient supplement especially designed for the preconceptual period, including folic acid whose requirements more than double during pregnancy.

Folic acid is essential for the healthy development of the nervous system and taking folic acid supplements can reduce the risk of certain congenital problems (neural tube defects) by as much as 72 percent. Folic acid intake needs to be increased by all women who are even just thinking of planning a pregnancy, as they are most effective when taken for three months before conception and in the first 12 weeks of pregnancy.

To prevent a first occurrence of neural tube defect: all women thinking of having a baby should eat more folate rich foods – including those fortified with folic acid – and take a dietary supplement of 0.4 milligrams (400 micrograms) of folic acid per day.

To prevent a recurrence of neural tube defect: women who have previously had a child with a neural tube defect should take 4 milligrams of folic acid supplements (or 5 milligrams – available on prescription – if lower dose is not available) daily, starting at least three months before conception and continuing until at least the twelfth week of pregnancy.

Taking a multi-vitamin and mineral supplement especially designed for the preconceptual period and which contains folic acid is the best option to guard against lack of other important nutrients. This is especially important if you follow a restricted diet (e.g. vegetarian or vegan) in which case you may need to seek professional dietary advice. New research suggests that natural vitamin E (d alpha tocopherol) is transported across the placenta 3.5

No one mentioned to me the importance of taking folic acid supplements. Not even my GP or the doctor at the hospital. What if I'd had a baby with spina bifida as a result? Doctors should be made to give this sort of information to their patients at every opportunity. Liz

I read a book [*Super Baby*, Dr Sarah Brewer (Thorsons)] about increasing your baby's intelligence in the womb, and decided to take an essential fatty acid supplement during the preconceptual period and throughout pregnancy, to help his brain development. I know it's a politically correct minefield, but if we are happy to ensure optimal physical growth of a baby in the womb, surely we should do all we can to optimise intelligence, too? Sonia

times more effectively than synthetic vitamin E (dl alpha tocopherol) so look for supplements supplying the 'd' form rather than the 'dl' form if possible.

Consider taking evening primrose oil (500mg-1g per day) as many women are deficient in essential fatty acids, and these are important building blocks needed for the healthy development of all your baby's cell membranes including those in the brain.

New essential fatty acid supplements are now also available that are especially designed for pregnancy and include evening primrose oil plus essential fatty acids derived from fish oils (e.g. Efanatal), or essential fatty acids derived from microalgae (e.g. Neuromins – available in the US) or tuna oil (Milkarra). These may be taken when planning a pregnancy, while expecting and when breast-feeding.

Alcohol

Try to avoid alcohol altogether during the three months before trying to conceive, and throughout pregnancy if you can. Alcohol is a cell poison that becomes concentrated in the cells of a developing baby to produce higher levels than in the mother. The tiny liver bud only starts developing a month after conception and these first four weeks – often before you are even aware you are pregnant – are one of the most vulnerable times for alcohol-induced foetal damage.

Regularly drinking even small amounts of alcohol can increase the risk of early miscarriage, and of miscarriage during the fourth to sixth months of pregnancy. Excessive alcohol intake is associated with a series of congenital abnormalities known as foetal alcohol syndrome, which include multiple facial abnormalities, congenital heart disease and low intelligence. Research suggests that if a woman regularly drinks two or three units per day throughout pregnancy there is an 11 percent chance that her baby will develop foetal alcohol syndrome. This risk rises to 19 percent with four units per day and to 30 percent in women who drink more than five units daily. A pregnant woman who regularly drinks more than nine units of alcohol per day is almost certain to have an affected child. Binge drinking is also harmful and increases the risk of developmental abnormalities. Many women are happy to give up alcohol as soon as their pregnancy is confirmed, but by then some damage may already have occurred if alcohol intake was high on at least one occasion.

Some studies (but not all) suggest that *low* intakes of alcohol (up to 8 units in a week) are not harmful during pregnancy. The best advice is to avoid alcohol altogether in the preconception period (at least three months) and for the first three months of pregnancy. If you find it difficult to go without alcohol after this, the odd drink (one or two units) once or twice a week during the later stages of pregnancy is unlikely to cause serious developmental harm, but there may still be an increased risk of spontaneous miscarriage.

(**Note:** 1 unit alcohol = 100ml (one glass) of wine; or 50ml (one measure) of sherry; or

25ml (single tot) of spirit; or 300ml (1/2 pint) normal-strength beer.)

If you feel you need help to cut out alcohol, contact the national alcohol helpline on 0171 352 3001.

Smoking

If you are a smoker, the most important thing you can do if you are thinking of having a baby is to give up – long before you try to conceive. Ideally you should leave at least six months between stopping smoking and trying for a baby. Smoking in the immediate three months before conceiving and/or during pregnancy is harmful as it triples your risk of difficulty in conceiving. One study also found that twice as many females smoking ten or more cigarettes per day remained involuntarily childless after five years compared with women who did not smoke.

Smoking during pregnancy also increases your risk of a miscarriage by a third, and is linked to stillbirth, low-birth weight and sudden infant death. It also doubles the risk of your baby developing a childhood cancer such as leukaemia. Passive smoking is also a cause of asthma, chest infection, eczema and glue ear in young children.

These risks all increase if the father smokes as well (see p. 128).

Exercise

It is important to get fit before trying to have a baby. Lack of exercise and fitness may increase the likelihood of your experiencing excessive tiredness and weight gain, high blood pressure, raised glucose (sugar) levels during pregnancy and a difficult delivery.

Aim to take at least 30 minutes exercise every day that is brisk enough to raise a light sweat and leave you slightly breathless. Don't

I was worried that I would miss my daily half-bottle of wine once I wanted to have a baby. I managed not to have any alcohol during the month before trying to conceive, then found the very thought of wine made me feel quite nauseated once I was pregnant. I didn't miss it at all! Sarah

A friend told me that getting fit before having a baby would mean I got my figure back more quickly afterwards as my tummy muscles would be more toned. I think she was right – look at Pamela Anderson and Jerry Hall. Jenny

We were thinking about having a baby, but wanted to go to Thailand on holiday as well. I had talked to my practice nurse about preconceptual care, and she advised postponing getting pregnant until after the trip so I could have the vaccinations and malaria tablets I needed. She insisted on waiting until the first day of my next period before giving me the jabs. Trudy

overdo it however. If you didn't take much exercise during the last six months before conception, start your fitness programme with a brisk walking regime.

Infections

While infections during pregnancy are not common, they can have disastrous results, so it is better to be safe than sorry. Women who are in the preconceptual care period, or who are already pregnant, should avoid immunization with any vaccines containing live viruses. These viruses have been changed so they no longer cause serious disease. They still multiply in the body to stimulate immunity, however, which may possibly harm a developing baby. If you are planning to have a baby but need an immunization (e.g. against Rubella), you should ensure that you use adequate contraception before, during and for three months after the vaccination.

While you can protect yourself against Rubella by having an antibody test and, if this is negative, being immunized, it is less easy to protect yourself against other infectious diseases that may be harmful to a developing baby. It is therefore a good idea to avoid anyone who is unwell with an infection, especially a flu-like illness. You should especially avoid anyone with chickenpox or shingles throughout the preconceptual period and pregnancy. If you do come into contact with a person who has chickenpox or shingles during the immediate preconceptual care period, or during pregnancy, seek medical help straight away. An injection of anti-Varicella zoster immunoglobulin (antibodies) may be needed to help protect both you and your future child.

Listeria

Listeria is an infection caused by a type of bacteria common in cattle, pigs and poultry. It can cause a flu-like illness in humans up to six weeks after exposure. This is especially harmful in pregnancy and is linked with miscarriage, preterm delivery and severe illness in the newborn such as meningitis and pneumonia. Women who are thinking about having a baby, and those who are pregnant, should avoid foods with a high listeria risk. Listeria is usually destroyed by pasteurization but if food is infected and then refrigerated, listeria continues to multiply. Avoid:

- any cheese made from unpasteurised milk

- ripened, soft cheeses (e.g. Brie, Camembert, Cambozola)
- blue-veined cheeses (e.g. Stilton, Roquefort, Blue Shropshire, Blue Brie, Dolcelatte)
- goat or sheep's milk cheeses (e.g. Feta, Chèvre)
- undercooked or raw meat products
- cook-chill meals and ready-to-eat poultry unless thoroughly re-heated
- all types of pâté
- ready-prepared coleslaw and salads
- unpasteurized milk or dairy products
- all foods past their 'best by' date
- rolls and sandwiches containing any of the above.

All pasteurized hard Cheddar-type cheeses are safe, as are cottage cheese, soft processed cheese spreads and cream cheese.

Listeria can also be passed on through contact with infected, live animals so avoid any that are obviously unwell.

Toxoplasmosis
Toxoplasmosis is an infection caused by a single-celled organism (protozoon) that can be caught from eating raw or undercooked meat, unwashed fruit and vegetables, drinking unpasteurized milk, or from handling cats' faeces. Infection is not dangerous to the healthy adult or child but may cause congenital abnormalities if caught during early pregnancy as well as increasing the risk of miscarriage and stillbirth. If a pregnant woman contracts toxoplasmosis, there is a 40 percent risk that her baby will be affected and, of these, 10 percent will have serious problems as a result.

To reduce the risk of toxoplasmosis:

- Avoid emptying cat litter trays during the preconceptual period and while pregnant. If you have to handle cat litter, use thick, disposable gloves and wash your hands thoroughly afterwards with an antiseptic solution.
- Always wash your hands thoroughly after handling cats and avoid close contact with any cat that is obviously unwell.
- Wear gloves when gardening and always wash your hands well afterwards.
- Avoid eating raw meat (e.g. steak tartar), raw fish (e.g. sushi) and raw cured meat (e.g. Parma ham, salami) and related products,

We were going to France on holiday while trying for a baby. My husband, who is a GP, insisted I avoided all of the local French cheeses and pâtés while we were there because of the risk of listeria. As I was also banned from drinking wine, the holiday was less enjoyable than usual. The sacrifices were all worth it however. I wasn't tempted to cheat once.
Rebecca

I had a discharge and decided to get it checked out before becoming pregnant. Lucky I did. I turned out to have a bacterial imbalance [anaerobic vaginosis] that could have caused a miscarriage or premature labour. The antibiotics I had to take couldn't be given in pregnancy, either, so it was just as well I got sorted out first.
Kimberly

and wash hands thoroughly after handling raw meat.

- Cook all meat thoroughly.
- Wash all fruit and vegetables before eating.
- Avoid unpasteurized milk – especially goats' milk and related products.
- Consider using frozen rather than fresh meat as freezing kills the reproductive cysts of toxoplasmosis.

Sheep and lambs are a source of toxoplasma as well as other organisms associated with recurrent miscarriage. Women who are thinking about having a baby, and those who are pregnant, should avoid contact with sheep, especially newborn lambs and ewes who are pregnant or milking. Farmers' wives and shepherdesses should handle work clothing with gloves, even when washing it, and keep the clothing away from kitchen work surfaces.

For more information about toxoplasmosis, contact the Toxoplasmosis Trust (see Resources, page 241).

Genito-urinary infections
It is worth visiting a genito-urinary medicine (GUM) clinic for a routine check-up before trying to have a baby, especially if you have noticed a vaginal discharge. One common vaginal infection, bacterial vaginosis, causes up to 50 percent of all vaginal infections in non-pregnant women, and up to 29 percent in pregnant women. It also increases the risk of miscarriage and preterm labour, so it is important to have this treated before trying to conceive.

A GUM clinic will also screen you for chlamydia and other genital infections that are best treated before a pregnancy. Chlamydia often causes no symptoms in the early stages, and slowly spreads up the female genital tract to cause inflammation and scarring of the fallopian tubes – a condition known as Pelvic Inflammatory Disease (PID). It has been estimated that as many as one in six women born between 1945 and 1954 have had symptomatic PID by the age of 30. PID can also cause difficulties in conceiving (in 13 percent of women who have had a single attack of PID) and the risk of ectopic pregnancy (implantation of a fertilized egg outside the womb, e.g. in a fallopian tube) is seven times greater in women who have had an attack of PID. You should therefore never ignore an abnormal vaginal discharge just in case it is a sign of infection. If chlamydia infection is present during pregnancy, there is an increased risk of miscarriage and preterm delivery. The baby is likely to pick up the infection during childbirth, developing sticky eyes (conjunctivitis), middle ear infection, genital infection or pneumonia. In many cases, this is the first sign that the mother is infected.

A GUM clinic will also provide information if you suffer from recurrent genital herpes. You may need to be screened regularly every week from the 36th week of pregnancy until delivery to ensure the infection does not reactivate at the time of childbirth. If it does, you will usually be advised to have an elective Caesarean section to protect your baby from infection. If your baby were to contract a herpes virus infection during birth, it could cause serious neonatal illness including meningitis and septicaemia. This risk is greatest during a primary attack, in which the infection is caught around the time of delivery, as you will not have had time to make protective antibodies that would help to protect your baby, as is the case with recurrent herpes infections. There is no reason why a woman with recurrent herpes who has no sores and is not shedding virus at the time of delivery (i.e. negative swabs) should not have a normal vaginal delivery, however.

If you have genital warts, you should ideally have them treated before thinking about having a baby – but you must let the doctor at the GUM clinic know if there is any chance of pregnancy or if you plan to have a baby in the very near future. Some anti-wart virus treatments (podophyllin) are potentially harmful to a developing baby, and you will therefore need to have the warts frozen or burned off instead. Try not to leave your warts untreated as hormone changes occurring during pregnancy can make them grow much larger than usual.

I had a few genital warts appear during pregnancy and assumed treatment would make them go away quickly, as before. Because I was pregnant however, they could only freeze them and they started to grow bigger. I had to go in every week for treatment until I was 32 weeks pregnant. The consultant said the aim of treatment was just to stop them growing any bigger – they can apparently reach the size of golfballs in pregnancy – not to make them go away. Once I had my baby, they quickly shrank and disappeared. Gemma

Some women prefer to have an HIV test before trying for a baby, to put their mind at rest. This again is something you can discuss

I was diagnosed with chlamydia after my baby was born prematurely with conjunctivitis. Luckily she's fine now, but if I had had a check-up at the clinic before getting pregnant, our months of worry could have been avoided. Jane

I have had recurrent genital herpes since the age of 24. I always knew there was a risk of the baby catching it during birth and was keen to have a Caesarean as a result. The consultant wanted to wait and let me deliver normally but I wasn't keen on this. Not surprisingly the worry of it all brought on another attack at 38 weeks, so my baby was delivered by elective Caesarean and was fine. Nita

I had to have my genital warts cut away under local anaesthetic when I was 20 weeks pregnant. They had grown so large they were going to interfere with childbirth. I felt so embarrassed, but the nurses, midwives and doctors were brilliant. Mandy

I worked as a prostitute before and during pregnancy. I had no choice – I needed the money. I was very careful however, and only went with a few long-standing clients. We always used condoms and spermicide. I'm not proud of what I did, and know I could have put my baby at risk. I had regular check-ups and remained clean throughout. Susan

with the GUM clinic, which will counsel you and perform the test if you wish. All visits to a GUM clinic are confidential, and your GP does not have to be informed.

Your main protection against sexually transmissible diseases is to practice safe sex. If your lifestyle, or that of your partner, puts you at risk of a sexually transmissible disease, it is important to protect yourself by using condoms – until you have both been checked and are given the all clear – before trying for a baby.

Drugs

When thinking about having a baby, it is important to avoid taking all but the most essential drugs. Even over-the-counter medicines carry risks and may interfere with conception and foetal development.

Surveys suggest that nine out of ten women take one or more drugs (over-the-counter or on prescription – herbal remedies, non-steroidal anti-inflammatory drugs, cod liver oil) during pregnancy. Many take up to three drugs with the potential to harm their developing baby, without realizing the risks involved. The chances on average of having a baby with a developmental defect are one in 20. Taking at least one prescription drug during pregnancy increases the risk threefold so there is a one in seven chance of causing a birth defect.

Prescription drugs

When thinking about having a baby, you need to make sure any doctor you consult knows you are contemplating parenthood. You need to find out which drugs you may safely continue taking and which should definitely be stopped or changed.

Drugs are sometimes essential during the preconceptual period and pregnancy, but it is usually possible to prescribe drugs known to be relatively safe, and to keep the dose as low as possible.

Many anti-epileptic drugs, for example, can cause problems as they interfere with the way folic acid (see page 117) works. It is therefore vital to seek specialist advice from a consultant gynaecologist and/or neurologist before trying to conceive to ensure that you are prescribed the safest drugs possible, that your folic acid intake can be adjusted, and you can be informed of all the risks involved before deciding whether or not to go ahead and conceive.

Over-the-counter drugs

All women thinking about having a baby, and those who are already pregnant, should also avoid over-the-counter drugs unless absolutely necessary – even those you might think are safe such as antacids, sports gels, painkillers and cough medicines can cause problems. If you are considering taking a drug, always check with a pharmacist beforehand to see if it is known to cause any problems during pregnancy.

Drugs of abuse
Avoid all illicit drugs. Some research suggests that at least one in ten developing babies in some countries are exposed to illegal drugs in the womb such as cannabis, amphetamines, cocaine, crack and heroin. These can affect foetal brain development, future emotional behaviour and increase the risk of congenital abnormalities, miscarriage, stillbirth and low birth weight. Babies born to addicted mothers will be addicted, too, and have to go through a process of withdrawal which carries a one in three risk of death in the first few weeks after birth.

Cocaine and crack can shut down blood supply to the womb and therefore to the baby almost completely, depriving it of oxygen and other essential nutrients. Damage to your baby can occur within three days after conception, so users need to stop using cocaine several weeks before they stop using contraception. The combination of cocaine and alcohol is particularly harmful.

Heroin addiction triples the risk of miscarriage or stillbirth, and quadruples the risk of premature labour and growth retardation.

Amphetamines can cause heart and other defects, and long-term use is linked with poor growth, preterm delivery, stillbirth and sudden infant death syndrome. Withdrawal symptoms can also occur.

Cannabis can cause preterm labour, low birth weight, tremor (shakes in the baby) and abnormal brain function.

For future fathers

It takes an average of 74 days for a newly divided primitive sperm cell to mature in the testes. Each sperm then takes around 20 days to travel through the 4-6 metre- (13-20 foot-)long tube (epididymis) at the head of each testicle during which it gains motility and becomes free-swimming. Motile sperm then spend another six days in the vas deferens, on average, before ejaculation, adding up to 100

I was referred to an obstetrician for preconceptual advice because of the tablets I was on for epilepsy. I had to take extra folic acid, and have regular check-ups and scans throughout the pregnancy. It was a bit frightening, and I was glad when it was all over and the baby was normal. Gopal

After trying for a baby for over a year, we were told my sperm count was low. This came as a complete shock as I'm hairy, well endowed, play rugby and am very masculine in every other way. I was given a nutritional programme to follow, vitamins and mineral supplements to take, and was advised to avoid alcohol (I've always been a non-smoker), throw away my tight underpants and douche my testicles with cold water three times a day. After three months, my sperm count came up and we started trying again. My wife conceived three months later. P

days of development in which a future father can take steps to keep the sperm destined to produce his future child as healthy as possible. These steps will help to reduce sperm abnormalities, such as the number of sperm with:

- unusually large or small heads
- two heads and one tail
- sluggishness, tending to swim round in circles or in a zig-zag path instead of going straight
- a tendency to clump together and hardly move at all (if clumping affects 20 percent or more of sperm, conception may prove difficult).

These abnormalities all contribute to infertility, although it is estimated that as many as one in ten sperm can be abnormal without loss of fertility. Unfortunately, sperm quality seems to be falling although the reason for decreased sperm count and increased abnormal sperm is unknown. It is now considered normal to find up to 40 percent of sperm in the ejaculate with architectural abnormalities or reduced motility. Relatively simple dietary and lifestyle changes can, however, significantly improve sperm quality and quantity.

Temperature
Sperm production is very sensitive to temperature, which is why the testicles hang outside the abdomen in the equivalent of a cool bag. The ideal temperature for sperm production is 32°C (89.6°F) – five degrees below normal body temperature of 37°C (98.4°F). Excess heat can quickly reduce sperm quality and men taking a hot bath (at say 43-45°C/109.4-113°F) for only half an hour a day have been found to have lower sperm counts than normal.

The style of underwear you choose is also important. Tight, bikini-type briefs – especially those made from man-made fibres – can reduce sperm counts by as much as 20 percent, sperm motility by as much as 21 percent and semen volume by as much as 12 percent. These effects are due to the damaging effects of excess heat and static electricity. In contrast, loose cotton boxer shorts help to keep the testes cool and do not generate static electricity so sperm quality improves over several months. It is therefore worth wearing cotton boxer shorts for at least six months before trying to father a child.

Vitamins and minerals for potential fathers

It is estimated that 40 percent of sperm damage is due to the harmful effects of free radicals. These are harmful by-products of metabolism that carry a small electric charge. They collide with cell structures – including genes – in an attempt to neutralize this charge through a chemical process called oxidation. Every cell in the body – including sperm cells – is estimated to receive over 10,000 free radical attacks per day, and the number is far greater in those who smoke or are exposed to environmental pollutants. Your main protection against free-radical attack comes from dietary antioxidants which mop them up and neutralize them before they can do any harm.

Genetic abnormalities in the offspring are more usually associated with abnormalities in the sperm than in the egg. This is probably due to the greater number of cell divisions needed to form a sperm (an estimated 380, compared with only 23 cell divisions needed to produce an egg). Cell division is the time when genetic accidents are most likely to occur, and the vast majority of these are linked with free-radical attack. It's therefore a good idea to ensure that your diet is full of antioxidants by eating as much fresh fruit and vegetables as possible. Supplements will also help.

The most important dietary antioxidants are:

- vitamin A and betacarotene
- vitamin C
- vitamin E
- selenium.

Lesser antioxidants that are also important include:

- riboflavin
- copper
- manganese
- zinc.

Vitamin C: a water-soluble antioxidant present in semen at concentrations eight times higher than those in blood. As well as having a powerful antioxidant effect, vitamin C also helps to stop sperm from clumping together and becoming inactive. Good dietary sources include citrus fruits, berries, guava, peppers, paw-paw, mangoes, kiwi fruit and green leafy or sprouting vegetables such as broccoli. Consider taking vitamin C supplements (500mg twice daily) for at least 100 days before trying to father a child. This has been shown to increase sperm count by 34 percent, reduce sperm clumping by 67 percent and reduce the number of abnormal sperm by 33 percent.

Vitamin E: a powerful fat-soluble antioxidant that helps to prevent cell membranes from free-radical attack. Vitamin E is also needed for flexibility of sperm cell walls, which is important in motility, and to stop sperm clumping together. Good dietary sources include seed and nut oils, avocado, wheatgerm oil and seafood. Consider taking vitamin E supplements (400 i.u daily) for at least 100 days before trying to father a child.

Zinc: an antioxidant that also plays a major role in sperm fertility. It is so important in fact, that each male ejaculate contains around 5mg zinc – one third of the recommended daily intake for adults. The head of each sperm contains a small bag of chemicals (acrosome) that are used to drill a hole through the 'eggshell' during fertilisation. If these enzymes are discharged too early, the sperm becomes incapable of penetrating the egg and this is thought to be a relatively common cause of male infertility. Zinc helps to keep the acrosome intact and stops it bursting open too early. Zinc also damps down the activity of sperm, helping them to conserve their energy for when it is needed. Once in the female tract, zinc levels are low, and as a result, the sperm become supercharged and dash off to find an egg. Lack of zinc is relatively common and contributes to male infertility. Unfortunately, regular sex reduces zinc levels even further.

It is easy to check your zinc levels. Test for zinc deficiency by obtaining a solution of zinc sulphate (5mg/5ml) from a chemist. Swirl a teaspoonful in your mouth. If the solution seems tasteless, zinc deficiency is likely. If the solution tastes furry, of minerals or slightly sweet, zinc levels are borderline. If it tastes strongly unpleasant, zinc levels are normal.

Good dietary sources of zinc include seafood (especially oysters), nuts, seeds and wholegrains.

Smoking and sperm

Chemicals in cigarette smoke can directly damage sperm and also increase production of free radicals. As a result, fathers who smoke are, sadly, more likely to produce offspring with genetic defects, with double the risk of cleft palate (harelip), heart and urinary tract abnormalities, and at least twice the risk of childhood cancers such as leukaemia and brain cancer. It is therefore vital for a prospective father to stop smoking long before he thinks about fathering a child. High-dose antioxidants will also help to minimize sperm damage (see above).

Alcohol and sperm

Excessive alcohol intake (more than 3-4 units per day) can reduce formation of sperm by lowering testosterone levels and – long-term – can even shrivel the testicles. As much as 40 percent of male infertility has been attributed to alcohol intake, even in moderate amounts.

In one study involving men with low sperm counts, 50 percent returned to normal within three months of avoiding alcohol completely. Ideally men should avoid alcohol for at least a month, and preferably three months, before trying to father a child, or at least stick to no more than 3-4 units per day although this may still compromise fertility.

Stress

Stress quickly reduces sperm count and, in severe cases, can stop sperm production altogether due to the way stress affects hormone levels. It is therefore important for men thinking about fathering a baby to take time out for rest and relaxation, and to avoid undue tension.

Drugs and sperm

Many drugs available on prescription, over-the-counter and those that are illegal, have a damaging effect on sperm. Use of all drugs should be avoided as much as possible when trying to father a child, and for at least 100 days beforehand. Also try to limit yourself to no more than three caffeine-containing drinks per day.

Exercise and sperm

While it is important to keep fit, future fathers should not over-train as regular, strenuous exercise can cause a dramatic drop in sperm counts – sometimes by up to 50 percent in fitness fanatics. Excessive training also increases the number of immature, non-fertile sperm found in semen. Keep to a sensible training

After training for a marathon, I was whippet thin and ultra fit, but sub-fertile. It took six months for my sperm count to recover to the point where we could think about having a family. John

I had mumps as a teenager and overheard the doctor telling my parents I may not be able to have children. I lived in fear for years without telling anyone. Eventually I met a girl I wanted to marry and requested a sperm count at a private clinic. The result was normal. I wish I'd had it done years ago so all that worry could have been avoided. James

programme, and avoid running marathons if you want to maximize your chances of successfully fathering a child.

Infections and sperm

Men suffering from non-specific urethritis (NSU) which is an infection of the urinary tube (urethra) have been linked with lower sperm count, lower sperm motility and a higher percentage of abnormal sperm than men who are free from the infection. If you notice any unusual discharge, soreness or other symptoms at the end of the penis, it is important to attend a GUM clinic for a full screen before thinking of fathering a child.

Many men worry that having had mumps can affect their fertility. The mumps virus causes inflammation of one testicle in up to one in three men during the attack – it is rare for both testicles to be affected, although no one knows why. When this occurs before puberty, complete recovery occurs. If mumps infection occurs after puberty, sperm production in the infected testicle usually falls and the testicle may shrink. Because the other testicle continues to function normally, this does not usually affect fertility. In one study, men who had had mumps as adults were found to have higher numbers of abnormal sperm and lower sperm motility, but all had sperm counts within the normal, fertile range. Following a preconceptual programme and taking antioxidant supplements will help to maximize your chances of success.

Examining your testicles for lumps

Testicular cancer is becoming more widespread – around 1,400 new cases are diagnosed every year and it is the most common form of cancer in men aged 20-34. It is therefore vital that men examine their testicles regularly for lumps. Testicular examination is best done in the bath when you are warm and relaxed. Hold a testicle gently between the thumb and fingertips of both hands. Slowly bring the thumb and fingertips of one hand together while relaxing the fingertips of the other. Alternate this action so the testicle glides smoothly between both sets of fingers. This lets you assess the shape and texture of the testis – it is normal to feel a soft structure (epididymis) at the top of each testicle towards the back. Repeat with the other testicle. Each should feel soft and smooth – like a boiled egg without its shell. If you notice any lumps or irregularity tell your doctor straight away.

Weight

Excess weight reduces male fertility as fatty tissue can break down circulating sex hormones into oestrogen. Excess fat can also raise scrotal temperature enough to reduce sperm count. It is therefore worth trying to get fit and lose excess weight as part of a male preconceptual care programme.

For you both

The following preconceptual advice is relevant for both potential parents:

Genetic counselling

If genetic abnormalities have previously occurred in the family of anyone thinking about having a baby one day, genetic counselling will help to assess whether or not future offspring have an increased risk of certain conditions. Reliable tests are now available for a number of genetic conditions, including cystic fibrosis. This is also important for marriages between cousins, as the risk of severe disability in the offspring of first-cousins is one in ten (three times higher than normal) due to a higher chance that offspring will inherit the same faulty gene from both parents.

Environmental pollutants

Both potential mothers and fathers should take steps to avoid environmental toxins such as lead exhaust fumes, mercury, industrial chemicals and agricultural herbicides, pesticides, fungicides, growth enhancers and fertilizers. Many such chemicals can have harmful effects on both egg and sperm, and have been implicated in falling sperm counts. They can also affect the development of a baby in the womb. Use the following suggestions to try and help reduce your exposure to environmental chemicals long before deciding to have a baby:

- Eat organic wholefoods where possible – especially milk and dairy products.
- Cut down on your consumption of animal fats.
- Avoid tinned and processed foods.
- Eliminate all dietary additives.
- Wash all vegetables, fruit and salad thoroughly, and peel as many

as possible.

- Eat garlic, yoghurt, bananas and pectin-containing fruits to help reduce absorption of dietary toxins.
- Use a water filter: an activated-carbon filter can extract chlorine while a reverse-osmosis water treatment system is needed to remove nitrates and dissolved toxic metals (e.g. lead, aluminium, cadmium, mercury). Alternatively, consider drinking bottled water from a source that provides an analysis or certification of purity.
- Avoid heavy traffic and inhaling exhaust fumes – keep car windows closed in traffic jams.
- Avoid mercury amalgam tooth fillings if at all possible (but old mercury amalgam fillings should not be removed in the immediate preconceptual care period, or during pregnancy).
- Do not burn waste rubbish, especially newspapers, magazines and plastics.
- Switch to lead-free petrol and a car fitted with a catalytic converter.
- Avoid any sheep-dipping activity or contact with dipped sheep.
- Avoiding close contact with agricultural sprays.
- Avoid routine x-rays.

Hair mineral analysis may indicate whether you have a particular toxic metal problem. You can also have your domestic drinking water analysed for toxic metals such as lead from old pipes.

Contraception
Family planning is an essential part of wanting to have a baby – one day. Contraception helps to ensure you start trying for a baby when you are ready and in the peak of health following a preconceptual care programme. Women thinking about having a baby may be happy to continue with their current method of contraception or may prefer to switch to an alternative – e.g. a non-hormonal method or natural family planning – in the run-up to trying for a baby. Ultimately only you can decide which method of contraception is right for you as a couple, but do take advice from your doctor, surgery nurse or family planning clinic.

The following table shows typical effectiveness rates for various methods of contraception (allowing for some human error) to help you decide which method is right for you based on their reliability in use:

Method	Typical Failure Rate
No contraception	85 percent
Withdrawal	19 percent
Natural family planning (symptothermal method)	up to 15 percent
Fertility awareness computer (Persona)	6 percent or more
Diaphragm/cap	up to 18 percent
Spermicides alone	21 percent
Sponge	up to 25 percent
Male condom	up to 15 percent
Female condom	up to 15 percent
Coil (IUCD)	1 percent-2 percent
Progestogen coil (intra-uterine system)	< 1 percent
Combined pill	<1-3 percent or more
Mini pill	<1-4 percent or more
Depot progestogen injection	<1 percent
Progestogen implant (Norplant)	<1 percent-2 percent
Female sterilization	< 1 percent
Male sterilization	< 1 percent
Morning-after pill	up to 4 percent
Morning-after IUCD	up to 2 percent

Many women decide to avoid hormonal methods of contraception in the months before trying for a baby to get it out of their system. While there is no evidence that getting pregnant immediately after using hormone contraception is harmful, many women prefer to give their body time to get back into its normal cycle before trying

I was using Persona as method of contraception before trying for a pregnancy. Once I was ready to get pregnant, I continued to use it but this time made love on the days it told me I shouldn't to help me get pregnant. Fatima

to conceive.

One of the best methods of contraception to use if you are thinking about having a baby in the near future is Natural Family Planning or fertility awareness. This is based on the recognition of signs and symptoms in a woman's body that ovulation is either about to, or already has occurred. These include:

- body temperature
- the position and texture of the cervix which becomes softer, pouts open and rises higher in the vagina during the fertile phase of your cycle
- changes in cervical mucus
- mid-cycle show of pink stained mucus which a few women experience
- mid-cycle pain occurring 24-48 hours before ovulation
- changes in breast sensitivity
- cyclical mood changes
- acne and other skin changes.

This helps you to focus in on your body's rhythms so you can pinpoint your most fertile period when the time is right to conceive. It is important to receive personal training in fertility awareness methods from a fertility awareness teacher (see Resources, page 235) as the techniques and calculations involved need complete understanding, especially if switching from a hormonal method of contraception. Keeping to strict guidelines may mean lengthy times of abstinence (or using a condom) and you need to be happy about this before deciding whether or not to proceed with the method. An excellent review of the method is included in *Fertility: Fertility Awareness and Natural Family Planning* by Dr Elizabeth Clubb and Jane Knight (David & Charles).

The method does involve you being perfectly comfortable with touching inside your body, feeling for your cervix and assessing vaginal discharge however. If you feel it is not the right method for you, switching to condoms (male or female) and using an ovulation predictor kit (see chapter 9) to help you get pregnant is another popular way to proceed.

Natural fertility awareness can also be combined with the fertility computer (Persona) to increase effectiveness.

The Pill

The combined oral contraceptive pill (COCP) contains two synthetic hormones, an oestrogen and a progestogen. It works by:

- inhibiting secretion of two hormones (FSH and LH) that are needed for an egg to mature each month, so that ovulation does not usually occur
- thickening cervical mucus so sperm cannot swim through so easily
- thinning the lining of the womb so if an egg does become fertilized, it is less likely to implant or develop
- slowing movement of sperm and eggs through the fallopian tubes connecting the ovaries and womb.

Many women taking the Pill wonder how soon they should come off it when they start thinking about having a baby. In general, taking the Pill does not seem to reduce fertility as was initially thought. Ninety percent of previously fertile women who stop using the Pill have a baby within 30 months. This is only two months longer than the average figures for women who had previously used the diaphragm or coil, and is thought to reflect the fact that many women stop the Pill 2-3 months before trying to conceive so the hormones are out of their system.

Another study looking at older women aged 30-35 years who had not previously had a child suggested that conception may be delayed for longer. After stopping the Pill, half of older women take up to a year longer to conceive compared to those of the same age who had previously used a diaphragm. The number of women in both groups who successfully became mothers within 72 months was similar however, suggesting there is no long-term effect on fertility. It does mean that a few older women who have used the Pill may face a delay of up to six years before conceiving once they decide to start a family. While there is no firm evidence that this is due to the Pill, some women may decide to stop using the Pill several years before they feel they want to start a family just in case. The Pill is undoubtedly an effective method of contraception, so you will have to weigh up the risk of becoming pregnant too soon if you switch to a less reliable method of contraception against that of delayed conception when the time comes to start trying.

Against these findings is the fact that fertility is at its greatest soon after stopping the Pill for some women – which is why

I stopped taking the Pill on my 37th birthday because I knew we wanted to start trying for a baby within the following year. We used condoms for a month, then threw them away as I became more and more concerned that age was against me. I needn't have worried. I gave birth exactly nine months later. Sarah

pregnancy can occur after missing just one dose. Because of this, the combined Pill is sometimes prescribed to women about to undergo assisted fertility techniques such as artificial insemination for infertility. Some research suggests that the chance of pregnancy is twice as high in women given the combined Pill before in-vitro fertilization, compared to those not taking the Pill. It may therefore be a shame to waste this period of super-fertility.

Unfortunately, the evidence is not clear cut, and if you are thinking about having a baby one day, you will need to do what you feel most comfortable with having discussed the issue with your partner and your doctor.

On balance, it is probably best for a woman who is thinking of having her first baby, or who has previously had no difficulty conceiving, to stop taking the combined Pill at least three months before trying for a baby. It is best to stop at the end of a pack of pills rather than in the middle. Women who have previously had difficulty conceiving, and who are now taking the Pill, should seek the advice of their obstetrician about how soon to stop the Pill before trying to conceive.

Chapter 9:

The Conception

Having thought you might like to have a baby one day, the time will eventually come when you are ready to conceive. This will usually be once your domestic, financial, social and career arrangements are satisfactory, your relationship is stable and you are ready to cement your love by creating a new life.

For some couples, conception is easy, while for others it becomes a frustrating and upsettingly elusive goal. Your average chance of conceiving is around 20 percent per month and the majority of couples will have successfully achieved a pregnancy within one year. Women who smoke have a lower chance of conceiving than non-smokers and fertility also falls with increasing age.

The fertile time of the month

Knowing exactly when you are fertile can significantly increase the odds of conception. The female fertile time is relatively short each month as an egg can only be fertilized from within six to 24 hours after it has been released at ovulation. As sperm can survive in the female reproductive tract for at least three to five days, this means that you need to make love within three to five days before ovulation and 12-24 hours afterwards to maximize your chances of conception. Making love during the other three weeks of your menstrual cycle will not lead to pregnancy. By recognizing the signs and symptoms associated with ovulation, or by using an ovulation predictor kit, you can increase your chances of success. The same signs and symptoms of fertility that are used to reduce risk of conception in natural, fertility-awareness methods of contraception (see page 134) can be used to increase chances of conception when the time is right to try.

Although a 28-day menstrual cycle is commonly referred to, many

When we stopped using condoms I went straight out and bought baby clothes, started thinking about the type of buggy I wanted, and planned how to decorate the nursery. If anyone had told me it would take three years before I conceived, I would have laughed at them. Those three years were the most soul-destroying time of my life. It seemed that everyone else in the world could get pregnant except me. I didn't get pregnant until I was near the top of the waiting list to see an infertility specialist. We never knew why I couldn't get pregnant initially – it happened quite quickly the second time round. Emma

women have cycles that are shorter or longer than this. In most cases, ovulation occurs around 14 days before your next period is due. If your cycle length is 28 days, this means you will tend to ovulate around day 14 of your cycle (where day 1 equals the first day of your last period). If cycle length is 35 days, you will tend to ovulate around day 21, and for a 21-day cycle, you will tend to ovulate around day 7.

Interestingly, more babies are conceived in November in Britain, the US, Austria, Belgium and Germany than in any other month – possibly related to the onset of long, dark winter nights. In Holland and Switzerland, the most popular month for conception is January, while in Sweden, more babies are conceived in August than in any other month.

Sperm counts

Following a preconceptual programme (see chapter 8) will help to maximize a man's sperm count, and minimize the percentage of abnormal or immotile sperm.

The average ejaculate contains 200-300 million sperm, although only 50 to 150 million of these eventually reach the upper fallopian tube and come into close contact with a newly ovulated egg. The average sperm count in the latter half of the 20th century has been estimated at a figure of around 66-77 million sperm per millilitre of semen. In general, the higher the sperm count and the higher the percentage of motile sperm, the higher the chance of conception. Studies suggest that if a man has a sperm count of less than 5 million motile sperm/ml, the chance of his partner eventually conceiving is 30 percent, and it will take an average of 11 menstrual cycles to achieve pregnancy. This chance increases to 70 percent for the partner of a man with a sperm count of over 60 million/ml, and will take an average of around six menstrual cycles for conception. Even men with very low sperm counts have been known to naturally father a child however. Bear in mind also that you only need a few healthy sperm to achieve success with some assisted conception techniques such as ICSI (intracytoplasmic sperm injection) in which a single sperm is injected under the shell of a harvested egg.

Interesting facts about sperm

- Sperm are produced at an average rate of 1,500 per second from each testicle.

- Sperm swim at a rate of 3mm per hour.
- A sperm lashes its tail 800 times to swim one centimetre.
- Sperm reach the fallopian tubes between 30 and 60 minutes after ejaculation into the female tract, helped along by eddy currents.
- Sperm normally only survive in the vagina for up to six hours due to the acidity of vaginal secretions.
- For sperm that find their way higher up the female reproductive tract, the average length of survival is three to four days.

How often should you make love?

Traditionally, couples were advised to make love every two or three days to maintain the male sperm count and to ensure an almost constant presence of sperm within the female tract. Some research now suggests that a couple may be able to maximize the chances of successful conception if the male abstains from ejaculation for seven to ten days before the female's most fertile time of the cycle. It was found that after seven days' abstention, sperm count and semen volume were significantly greater than if the men abstained for only three days, while sperm motility, viability and the percentage of abnormal forms stayed the same.

Interestingly, fertility experts have discovered that women usually ovulate at around 4 pm. The best time to make love may therefore be around lunchtime on the day ovulation is due.

A 1994 Gallup survey on behalf of First Response found that wanting to have a baby increases the romance in a relationship. Twenty-three percent of women questioned believed that trying for a baby made lovemaking more special, and this figure rose to 29 percent among men who hoped to become a father. Six percent of men hoped it would encourage their partner to take the lead in bed, while 25 percent of women admitted they would probably make love more often if they were planning to have a baby.

Age and conception

Female fertility does decline with increasing age. The average time taken to achieve a pregnancy for a healthy woman aged 25 years is two to three months compared with six months or longer for a woman ten years older. Having said that, more and more women are

My husband was told he might be infertile after contracting mumps at the age of 30. I married him knowing we might not have children, and never bothered using contraception as a result. After ten years, we now have two healthy children (both his!) although my partner's sperm count is still apparently in the infertile range. You only need one sperm, after all, so a count of fewer than 5 million seems more than adequate to me. Anne

I read in an article that you should make love at lunchtime to get pregnant. My partner and I snuck out of work and met in a local hotel – we did it for a laugh more than anything. I don't know if it worked or not, but I certainly fell pregnant that month! Joanne

I took out the Woman's Plan insurance with PPP at the age of 37 – mainly because it offered a certain amount of fertility treatment if I had difficulty conceiving after being a member for a set period of time. I thought of this as my safety net as I knew I wouldn't be trying for children until the age of 38, and was worried I wouldn't easily get pregnant. As a bonus, you also got a lump sum back during pregnancy after being a member for three years. Jane

I had my first baby at the age of 39 years. I was offered amniocentesis but decided not to take it. I reasoned that if the test was positive, I wouldn't contemplate having a termination so what was the point? Candice

waiting until later in life before deciding to have a baby, and more women are now having a baby in their early 30s than in their early 20s.

Unfortunately female fertility begins to fall around the age of 30. Egg cells (oocytes) start disappearing from the ovaries even faster after the age of 37, and those that remain are more likely to have genetic abnormalities. By the time a woman has reached her late 40s, the chances of natural pregnancy are small. The proportion of couples taking more than 12 months to conceive after first starting to try rises from 25 percent in the under-25s, to around 33 percent for women aged 25 to 29, and further still to 45 percent for those aged over 30.

Declining fertility is an important factor to bear in mind when deciding whether or not you still have time to postpone having a child, or whether your biological clock is running out of ticks. Pregnancy also becomes more risky as you get older. A woman aged over 40 runs a ten times greater risk of dying during pregnancy than a woman aged 20 to 24. The risks are still relatively small however, and translate into around 50 deaths per 100,000 older pregnant women compared with 5 per 100,000 younger women. The risk of miscarriage also increases with maternal age. The risk of miscarriage in women aged under 30 is just over 10 percent, but rises to 15 percent for women aged 37 years and to as much as 45 percent for women aged 45 years.

The risk of genetic defects also increases as the ovaries age – studies suggest that in women aged over 35, one in every three eggs that remain is abnormal. The risk of conceiving a child with Down's syndrome, for example, is 1 in 1,500 for a mother aged 25 years. At the age of 30, the risk increases to 1 in 800, and at 35 it is 1 in 300. By the age of 38, the risk increases to 1 in 180, by 40 years it is 1 in 100 and by the age of 45 it has risen dramatically to 1 in 30. As a result, amniocentesis (see chapter 10) to check the genetic make-up of the developing foetus early during pregnancy is offered to all women over the age of 35, and is also available for those with increased risk (e.g. due to family history) below that age.

There is some evidence that having taken the oral contraceptive Pill may help to reduce the risk of miscarriage. In one study of 585 couples planning a pregnancy, the number of years the woman had used the contraceptive Pill was directly linked with pregnancy outcome. In women who were aged over 30 years, who had used the

Pill for more than nine years, the risk of miscarriage was reduced fourfold, to 7 percent, compared with a risk of 28 percent for women aged over 30 who had not previously used the Pill. The researchers suggested that taking the Pill helps to preserve the number of follicles present in the ovaries. It is also possible that taking the Pill has helped to preserve the healthier eggs that would otherwise have been lost during the ovulations that were damped down by taking the Pill.

Predicting ovulation

Ovulation predictor kits are an accurate way of pinpointing your most fertile time of the month, thus maximizing your chance of conception. Tests are available over-the-counter from pharmacies for home use. They are easy to use, take only three to five minutes, and provide up to 99 percent accurate results. They work by measuring the amount of luteinising hormone (LH) in your urine. While this is always present in small amounts, it suddenly increases just before ovulation and triggers the release of an egg. Most women ovulate 12-36 hours after the sudden rise in LH is detected and, as the egg can usually only be fertilized for up to 24 hours after ovulation, having sex on the day the LH surge is detected will increase your chance of a successful outcome.

In approximately one out of every 13 menstrual cycles, a woman does not ovulate and therefore cannot become pregnant that month. This is perfectly normal and nothing to worry about. If you don't seem to ovulate for two or three consecutive cycles however, it is important to consult your doctor in case you need to investigate why you are not ovulating.

> After trying unsuccessfully for a pregnancy for six months, I decided to use an ovulator predictor kit. It soon became clear I wasn't ovulating, and this was confirmed with a blood test at the doctors. I was then referred to a consultant and prescribed a fertility drug to help stimulate ovulation. I got pregnant one month later, so I'm glad the kit helped to show something was wrong. If I hadn't used it, I would have had to wait two years before my GP would have referred me to the hospital for investigation of infertility. Susan

My second baby was conceived when I was aged 37 years. I decided to have an amnio' even though I knew it wasn't 100 percent accurate. There is no way I could cope with bringing up a handicapped baby and I would seriously have thought about having a termination if necessary. It was also nice knowing the sex of my baby in advance – I felt I bonded with my son better as a result. Sarah

My wife decided to stop taking the Pill three months before trying for a pregnancy. In the end, we kept worrying that perhaps she was losing her best eggs so we stopped using condoms as well. We now have a gorgeous son and I often think that he might not be here – or here in a different guise – if we had stuck to our original plan. Richard

Can you influence the sex of your baby?

Slightly more male babies are born than females – around 105 boys for every 100 girls. Because of a slightly higher rate of infant death among boys however, population proportions are roughly equal.

It is the sperm that determines a baby's sex. Each sperm contains either a female (X) sex chromosome, or a male (Y) chromosome, while each egg only contains a female (X) chromosome. If an X-sperm fertilizes the egg (X) a female baby results (XX), but if a Y-sperm fertilizes an egg (X) a male baby results (XY).

It is possible to improve on nature's odds and increase your chances of a child of selected sex. Scientific methods of separating male and female sperm rely on the fact that the X chromosome is heavier than the male, so they tend to swim more slowly, sluggishly yet persistently than sperm containing a Y chromosome. In contrast, male sperm carrying a Y chromosome tend to swim faster but with less stamina and tire more easily. All other things being equal, the race for the egg is usually won by the swifter Y chromosome – hence the slightly higher number of male babies born.

X- and Y-sperm can therefore be separated according to their different weights and speeds, by getting them to swim through special solutions or labelling them with fluorescent dyes or electric charges. Isolated sperm fractions may then be used for assisted-conception techniques. Success rates are rarely greater than 80 percent and results cannot be guaranteed. These techniques are only licensed for medical use such as reducing the risk of having a child with a hereditary, sex-linked disorder.

The following are just some of many traditional old-wives' methods offering advice on how to conceive babies of one sex or the other, although their success rates are unknown:

Tips to conceive a girl

- After menstruation, have frequent intercourse until at least 24 hours before ovulation. Then, avoid sex until at least a week after ovulation (use an ovulation predictor kit or natural fertility methods). This is said to increase the chance of fertilization with an X-sperm, which has greater staying power.

- Douche the vagina with a mildly acidic solution just before having sex. The solution is made by dissolving 5ml (1 teaspoon) of white vinegar in a pint of sterile, distilled water.

- Try to avoid the woman having an orgasm as stimulated secretions increase vaginal alkalinity.
- Try to ejaculate just inside the vagina, where conditions are more acidic, rather than higher up.

(It is also said that men who enjoy real ale are more likely to father daughters than men who prefer lager!)

Tips to conceive a boy

- Avoid intercourse during the four days just before ovulation. Plan to make love at or just after ovulation (use an ovulation predictor kit, or natural fertility methods). This helps to ensure the lighter, faster male sperm reach the egg first.
- Douche the vagina with a mildly alkaline solution just before having sex. The solution is made by dissolving 5ml (1 teaspoon) of sodium bicarbonate in a pint of sterile, distilled water.
- Ideally, the woman should have an orgasm just before ejaculation as stimulated secretions increase vaginal alkalinity.
- Try to ejaculate deep inside the vagina, preferably against the cervix, where conditions are more alkaline.

Previous termination of pregnancy

Sadly, the decision to terminate a pregnancy sometimes has to be made. It is important to know that any surgical procedure involving the womb does carry a small risk of complications such as infection, perforation or damage to the cervix. It is rare for a previous termination of pregnancy to affect future fertility however. Research involving over 9,000 women has found no difference in fertility rates between those who had previously had a termination compared with those who had not.

In the case of spontaneous miscarriage, the likelihood of recurrence will depend on the cause, but overall 95 percent are due to a non-recurring factor so the prognosis for future pregnancy is excellent.

The early signs of pregnancy

The egg is usually fertilized soon after ovulation, around two weeks before your next period is due. By the time your period is one day late, you will usually have been pregnant for around two weeks. As the fertilized egg burrows into the womb lining, the developing placenta starts to secrete a pregnancy hormone, human chorionic gonadotrophin (hCG). This helps to maintain early pregnancy by stopping your next period from occurring, and is detectable in your blood as early as 48 hours after conception and in the urine 72 hours after conception. This and other changes occurring in your body during early pregnancy produce symptoms that suggest you might be pregnant. These include:

- feeling increasingly tired, which is often one of the first clues
- a missed period or an unusually light one
- nausea and sometimes vomiting (not just in the morning)
- breast changes with tingling, tenderness and distension of superficial veins
- darkening and tingling of the nipples
- needing to pass water more frequently, including at nigh and, a tendency towards constipation
- having a strange, metallic taste in your mouth
- going off certain foods and craving others
- increased vaginal discharge.

Note, not every woman notices every symptom.

Pregnancy tests

Pregnancy tests work by detecting hCG in your urine during early pregnancy and are around 99 percent accurate. Use a home kit or take a sample of early morning urine to a pharmacist; you can carry out a pregnancy test from the first day of a missed period. Unfortunately, at least one in three fertilized eggs do not develop beyond the first 20 days, and some women will go on to experience a late period and the pregnancy test will revert to negative. This can obviously be upsetting, especially if you have had difficulty conceiving in the past. It is usually nature's way of stopping abnormal embryos from continuing to develop and does not mean you will continue to have problems maintaining an early pregnancy.

It is possible to test negative even though you are pregnant. Wait a week and, if your period still hasn't occurred, repeat the test again. If it is still negative, consult your doctor as soon as possible.

When is your baby due?

According to research from Denmark, it seems that experienced mothers don't plan for their baby to arrive around Christmas. They found that, out of 2 million births between 1960 and 1994, older women were significantly less likely than younger women to have their baby at Christmas time. As a result, many more first babies than subsequent babies were born in late December. Some women actively prefer December babies however.

Few women think about when their baby will actually be due when first thinking about conception – even fewer would consider putting off trying because their baby's birth might clash with important celebrations or events.

Even so, it is worth having a rough idea of when your baby will be due. The easiest way to estimate your baby's expected date of delivery is to take the *first* day of your last period, add on seven days, and subtract three months. (So if your last period started on 1 May, your baby would be due on: 1 May + 7 days – 3 months = 8 February.

The Obstetric Chart on page 146 does this calculation for you. Go to the date on which your last menstrual period started (top line). Underneath this is your estimated date of delivery, assuming a normal length of pregnancy.

Bear in mind that only one in 20 babies is actually born on the expected date given to the mother in early pregnancy – it is quite normal for delivery to occur within two weeks on either side.

Our first baby was born bang in the middle of the World Cup final. If I'd thought about it in advance, I would probably have suggested putting the conception off for a bit. But we didn't expect my wife to get pregnant quite so easily. David

Top Figures (bold) = First day of last menstrual period

Bottom Figures (light) = expected date of delivery

Jan	1	2	3	4	5	6	7	8	9	10	11	12	13	14	15	16	17	18	19	20	21	22	23	24	25	26	27	28	29	30	31	Jan
Oct	8	9	10	11	12	13	14	15	16	17	18	19	20	21	22	23	24	25	26	27	28	29	30	31	1	2	3	4	5	6	7	Nov

Feb	1	2	3	4	5	6	7	8	9	10	11	12	13	14	15	16	17	18	19	20	21	22	23	24	25	26	27	28				Feb
Nov	8	9	10	11	12	13	14	15	16	17	18	19	20	21	22	23	24	25	26	27	28	29	30	1	2	3	4	5				Dec

Mar	1	2	3	4	5	6	7	8	9	10	11	12	13	14	15	16	17	18	19	20	21	22	23	24	25	26	27	28	29	30	31	Mar
Dec	6	7	8	9	10	11	12	13	14	15	16	17	18	19	20	21	22	23	24	25	26	27	28	29	30	31	1	2	3	4	5	Jan

Apr	1	2	3	4	5	6	7	8	9	10	11	12	13	14	15	16	17	18	19	20	21	22	23	24	25	26	27	28	29	30		Apr
Jan	6	7	8	9	10	11	12	13	14	15	16	17	18	19	20	21	22	23	24	25	26	27	28	29	30	31	1	2	3	4		Feb

May	1	2	3	4	5	6	7	8	9	10	11	12	13	14	15	16	17	18	19	20	21	22	23	24	25	26	27	28	29	30		May
Feb	5	6	7	8	9	10	11	12	13	14	15	16	17	18	19	20	21	22	23	24	25	26	27	28	1	2	3	4	5	6	7	Mar

June	1	2	3	4	5	6	7	8	9	10	11	12	13	14	15	16	17	18	19	20	21	22	23	24	25	26	27	28	29	30		Jun
Mar	8	9	10	11	12	13	14	15	16	17	18	19	20	21	22	23	24	25	26	27	28	29	30	31	1	2	3	4	5	6		Apr

Jul	1	2	3	4	5	6	7	8	9	10	11	12	13	14	15	16	17	18	19	20	21	22	23	24	25	26	27	28	29	30	31	Jul
Apr	7	8	9	10	11	12	13	14	15	16	17	18	19	20	21	22	23	24	25	26	27	28	29	30	1	2	3	4	5	6	7	May

Aug	1	2	3	4	5	6	7	8	9	10	11	12	13	14	15	16	17	18	19	20	21	22	23	24	25	26	27	28	29	30	31	Aug
May	8	9	10	11	12	13	14	15	16	17	18	19	20	21	22	23	24	25	26	27	28	29	30	31	1	2	3	4	5	6	7	June

Sept	1	2	3	4	5	6	7	8	9	10	11	12	13	14	15	16	17	18	19	20	21	22	23	24	25	26	27	28	29	30		Sept
June	8	9	10	11	12	13	14	15	16	17	18	19	20	21	22	23	24	25	26	27	28	29	30	1	2	3	4	5	6	7		Jul

Oct	1	2	3	4	5	6	7	8	9	10	11	12	13	14	15	16	17	18	19	20	21	22	23	24	25	26	27	28	29	30	31	Oct
July	8	9	10	11	12	13	14	15	16	17	18	19	20	21	22	23	24	25	26	27	28	29	30	31	1	2	3	4	5	6	7	Aug

Nov	1	2	3	4	5	6	7	8	9	10	11	12	13	14	15	16	17	18	19	20	21	22	23	24	25	26	27	28	29	30		Nov
Aug	8	9	10	11	12	13	14	15	16	17	18	19	20	21	22	23	24	25	26	27	28	29	30	31	1	2	3	4	5	6		Sept

Dec	1	2	3	4	5	6	7	8	9	10	11	12	13	14	15	16	17	18	19	20	21	22	23	24	25	26	27	28	29	30	31	Dec
Sept	7	8	9	10	11	12	13	14	15	16	17	18	19	20	21	22	23	24	25	26	27	28	29	30	1	2	3	4	5	6	7	Oct

The Obstetric Chart above will calculate your baby's expected date of delivery. Go to the date on which your last menstrual period started (top line). Underneath this is your estimated date of delivery, assuming a normal length of pregnancy.

A professional on ...

I want to have a baby – why can't I conceive?

Most people assume it is very easy to get pregnant. For one in six people though, it is very difficult. Incredible as it may seem, with regular unprotected sex a couple with no fertility difficulties have, at best, a 20 percent chance of conceiving each month!

What can you do if you find that conception is difficult? The first step is to consult your GP. You should seek your GP's advice if you have been having regular unprotected sex for 12 months and pregnancy has not occurred. Wait no more than six months before seeing your GP if:

- you have absent or irregular periods
- you have had abdominal or pelvic surgery
- you are aged 35 or over
- your partner has had surgery in his groin region or has sustained an injury to his testicles
- either of you has had a sexually transmitted disease
- you are aware of a possible genetic reason for difficulty in conceiving.

Consulting your GP sounds easy, but is not. Deciding to try for a baby is a private matter. You may have shared your decision with close friends and family, but involving an impersonal third party is another matter. There is often also a sense of failure associated with an inability to conceive.

Dealing with remarks about starting a family can be difficult. You can say that you are not yet ready for a child, in which case you may get warnings about leaving it too late. You can be open and say you would like a child, but pregnancy has not occurred yet. This draws attention to your difficulties, with well-meaning people seeking information on your behalf or pointing out every article on infertility in the popular press. This is when you should quietly but firmly acknowledge that you are having difficulties and that you are seeking advice. Suggest to people that they can help by letting you get on with it unless you request their assistance, unless you yourself bring the subject of your difficulties into conversation. If this sounds difficult to do, try writing a letter. One of our members wrote just such a letter to her sister-in-law. It did not cause a family rift, but produced the desired reaction.

It is important to remember that you are not alone. Infertility is more common than people believe. Everyone has a part to play in life and a contribution to make to society. We are all valuable in our own right. Our value does not depend on our ability to attain parenthood. Hold on to this fact when things are rough and the road seems uphill all the way.

Although we use the term 'infertility', few people are truly infertile. It is usually a case of one or more problems reducing the already small 20 percent chance of conception each month.

Your GP should be able to take a medical history from you both and do some basic tests. He may refer you to a hospital. As infertility is a specialist area of medicine, you should ask to be referred to a specialist in reproductive medicine.

IVF (in-vitro fertilization) is probably the best known form of treatment. It is one of the advanced reproductive techniques that can only be performed in a centre licensed by the Human Fertilization & Embryology Authority. Not everyone who experiences infertility will need IVF. There are many less advanced but equally effective forms of treatment. The important thing is for your infertility to be thoroughly investigated and for you to be offered the most appropriate treatment.

You can help by gathering as much information as you can about infertility. Being an informed patient means you can work with your doctors in deciding the most appropriate option for you to follow. The stress involved is considerably reduced if you know what the tests and treatments are, what they are for and why they are offered to you.

Infertility can feel very isolating. It does not have to be. Many people have found it helpful to meet or talk with others who are also experiencing infertility. If you do not wish to go along to a local support group, counselling can also be very beneficial. Talking to a trained infertility counsellor about your feelings, your difficulties and your options helps you to manage the situation positively, to take control and decide the way forward. Licensed infertility clinics will have counselling available. Alternatively you can contact the British Infertility Counselling Association for details of trained infertility counsellors.

Most importantly, as you explore possible causes or treatment options try not to feel guilty or apportion blame. Share the challenge and support each other. Concentrate on your relationship. Make time for each other, have candlelit meals, share a bottle of wine, go for days out or visits to the cinema. Remember too that sex is for pleasure, not just for conception. Do not worry about timing sex for the 'right time of the month'. If you have sex regularly and enjoy it you are doing your part to have a baby. Most of those who go through infertility become parents and excellent parents at that.

Susan Rice, Chief Executive of ISSUE (the National Fertility Association)

ISSUE provides a regular magazine containing many articles and stories about infertility. Simply receiving the magazine reinforces the fact that you are not alone with the problem. In addition, ISSUE operates an evening telephone counselling service.

Gay parenting: Conception
by **Lisa Saffron**

Lesbians who plan to get pregnant by self-insemination do an incredible amount of advanced planning, as they need to arrange to get to a clinic or choose a sperm donor and arrange to meet him at the time when they are most fertile.

Donor insemination

This is the method of choice for lesbians. But it may take months or even years in the planning stages. The first step is to decide whether you want to go to a clinic or arrange for insemination with a known donor. There are advantages and disadvantages of going to a clinic:

Advantages

- There is no risk of HIV or STDs as donors are carefully screened. (However, all clinics are required by law to freeze the semen and this substantially reduces its chance of fertilizing an egg.)

- All donors are anonymous and neither you nor your child can ever learn their true identity. (Depending on your point of view, this may be an advantage or a disadvantage.)

Disadvantages

- You are given little information about the donors other than their physical characteristics which means that you are making a major decision about your child's genetic background with very little on which to base it.

- Pregnancy becomes a medical event, taken out of the personal and private setting of your home.

- You become subject to invasive medical procedures despite the fact that you are not suffering from a fertility problem.

- Many clinics are private and may charge as much as £450 per insemination.
- It can be difficult finding a clinic that will take you as many are prejudiced against lesbians and single women.

Self-insemination

The term 'self-insemination' is used to describe the informal, non-medical arrangement lesbians make with men willing to donate sperm. Often, but not always, the donors are gay men who are prepared to negotiate with you about the type of involvement they will have with the child. During planning you should ask yourself:

- Is it important to you that your child knows the identity of its genetic father?
- Would a known donor threaten the position of your partner if she will be sharing the parenting with you?
- Do you want the donor to play some role in the family (uncle figure, family friend) but not to have parental responsibility?
- Do you want to share parenting with the donor?

Once you've decided what kind of relationship you want with a donor, you can start the process of finding him, whether by advertising or through friends.

The planning process is necessarily lengthy and you could use this time to prepare your body for pregnancy using the preconceptual programme in chapter 8. It would also help for you to become familiar with your menstrual cycle so that when you start inseminating, you will do it at your most fertile time (see page 134).

The simpler the arrangements for getting the sperm to the woman while she is fertile, and within two hours of ejaculation, the more likely it is that the insemination will proceed smoothly. All too often, however, the arrangements become complicated and stressful. This is especially so where the donor remains anonymous. Intermediaries are then involved and the transfer of semen must be timed carefully to make sure the minimum of time passes between ejaculation and insemination.

Sperm donors

Any man who is trying to father a baby should be able to demonstrate that he is not putting the woman or the baby at risk of any transmissible illnesses or genetic conditions. Because of the long window period between exposure to the HIV virus and the first appearance of antibodies (detected in the HIV test), donors should be practising safe sex and be able to reassure the woman that they have not been doing anything which puts them at risk of HIV infection. It is worthwhile assessing the man's fertility by having a semen analysis done before you start inseminating (see page 138). The sperm should be plentiful, active and normal in shape. Specifically, there should be more than 50 million sperm per ml, more than 60 percent should be motile after one hour, and there should be less than 30 percent abnormally shaped sperm. If any one of these three criteria is not met, your chances of achieving pregnancy are much reduced.

Mike is a gay man who has donated sperm to several lesbians. He says:

Each time I've donated for a new woman, I've had another HIV test ... I was asked about my sexual practice and I think it's essential that women ask. You're talking about people's lives ... I'm having a sexual relationship (with a man) at the moment and it's as safe as it could possibly be. The woman I'm donating to knows all about that. Basically she has to trust me.

Karen and Traci are a lesbian couple who asked a gay man to be a donor. Traci says:

We decided to have a known donor because no matter how well we can parent a child, we don't want to take away the child's chance ever to know their father ... We advertised for a gay donor in the gay media. We were fairly sure early on about the man we chose ... Within a few meetings, there was absolute respect and trust and fondness. ... We both feel that he won't threaten our situation. He doesn't want to intrude upon our relationship. We discussed everything in great detail – religion, diet, even things like how important creative play is to all of us.

Karen says:

The man we have chosen will be the father, not just the donor. He wants to be a daddy at a distance and that's what we want. We will be the prime carers in that the child will live with us. The father will be invited for family celebrations, will look after the child at weekends and holidays and come to parents' evenings, but he sees us as making the day-to-day decisions. The child will have our last name and he's supportive of that. We agreed that his name would be on the birth certificate.

Eunice, co-parenting a child with lesbian partner, Stella, who conceived by self-insemination, says:

We were lucky with co-operative donors. We would give approximate dates for insemination from one month to the next and then confirm nearer the time. It took 18 months for Stella to get pregnant. I think that we always did something slightly different, each time thinking that we must have found the reason why it hadn't worked the time before. Initially friends did collections for us and Stella would inseminate at home, but we ended up collecting it ourselves and just doing it in the back of the car. This was much easier than it sounds and actually lightened things up as we ended up laughing at the ridiculous traffic situations we got into. This was the method that worked in the end. It could just be that our time had come and it would have worked anyway. Who knows?

Margaret is raising her daughter in a lesbian relationship with her partner Cecilia:

I got pregnant by donor insemination at a private clinic. I had fertility problems caused by polycystic ovaries so I felt I had no choice. In any case, I wanted the donor to be anonymous and not to have any worry about the risk of sexually transmitted diseases. I chose a Jewish donor involved in the film industry who reflected Cecilia's background. I conceived and had a lovely little girl.

Chapter 10:
Pregnancy

I enjoyed being
pregnant but as the
months passed by I
began to feel I just
wanted to get it over.
As long as our baby
had the regular
number of fingers and
toes, and looked like
most other babies I'd
be happy. Joy

I love being pregnant
and never feel as
physically well or
happy as when I am
expecting. That's the
main reason why we
have five children.
Jenny

When thinking about having a baby, one of the many things you will
wonder is how pregnancy itself will affect you. Every woman is
different. Some sail through pregnancy with few symptoms or
problems, while others feel lousy virtually the whole time. In general,
it seems the happier you are about being pregnant, the better you
will cope: researchers have found that women who are unhappy
about being pregnant report up to twice as many problems during
and after pregnancy as women who planned their pregnancy and
were happy about their decision to have a baby.

> When I was pregnant, I loved being the centre of attention and the
> feeling of power – being in control of every situation. I can't wait to
> be pregnant again, but we can't really afford it at present. Tina

Many good pregnancy books are available that explore pregnancy
and its effects in detail. It is worth buying one or two of these in
advance of your planned pregnancy so that you fully understand
what will happen, and read different case histories about how
different women have faired. Pregnancy is a natural experience. It is
not an illness, and for the majority of women everything will proceed
perfectly normally. It is important not to let yourself be cast in the
role of a patient – unless of course, that is how you want to play it.

> Being pregnant with my daughter was the worst experience of my
> life. I never want to go through it again, and am seriously
> considering sterilization. Unfortunately, this is putting a strain on my
> marriage as my husband would love to have a son. Lisa

Try not to be put off by horror stories – for most women, pregnancy
is a wonderful and exciting experience. The way pregnancy affects

you will be different from the way it affects your sister, mother or best friend, and it is worth remembering that in the majority of cases the long-term gains far outweigh any short term discomforts.

Weight gain

One of the most common things women ask about is how much weight they will put on during pregnancy. The way pregnancy affects your metabolism depends on the particular genes you have inherited.

Overall, you need an extra 70,000 kcals on top of your normal requirements, during your nine months of pregnancy. This is equal to 280 extra calories per day for 250 days, not counting the first month of pregnancy. This doesn't mean you have to eat an extra 280 kcals per day, however – most of the extra energy comes from decreased physical activity, and from the fact that your metabolism becomes more efficient so less energy is wasted as heat. The Department of Health recommends that pregnant women only need to eat an extra 200 kcals per day during the last three months of pregnancy. Women who were underweight at the beginning of pregnancy and those who do not reduce their levels of activity may need more.

The average weight gain during pregnancy is around 12.5kg (27.6lb) and is distributed as shown below.

Where the Weight is Gained	kg	(lb)
Your baby	3	(7)
Placenta	0.7	(1.5)
Amniotic fluid	0.9	(2)
Uterus	0.9	(2)
Breasts	0.5	(1)
Extra blood	1.5	(3-3.5)
Extra body fluid	1.5	(3-3.5)
Extra fat	2.5-3.5	(5-10)

Most obstetricians routinely weigh pregnant women, although others feel maternal weight is not a good indicator of foetal growth or well-being. Research shows that women of normal weight ideally

I put on five stone during my pregnancy, and was devastated to still look pregnant long after the delivery. I breast-fed my baby for nine months and slowly lost three stone during this time. I then started a concerted healthy eating and exercise programme and now only have ten pounds to go; looking after a young baby and running round after a toddler is a good way to lose excess weight.
Monica

need to gain between 11.5kg (25 lb) and 16kg (35 lb) for optimum growth and development of their baby. Women who are obese also need to gain between 7kg (9 lb) and 11.5kg (25 lb) for healthy development of their baby, even though they are very overweight to start with.

Try not to worry too much about weight gain during pregnancy. You may notice that you put on weight in unusual places, such as between your shoulders, on your upper back and around your knees as well as on your hips and thighs. This acts as an important energy store for when you start breast-feeding. Most women start to lose weight slowly while nursing, but it is important not to try to diet until your baby is weaned.

For most women – whether they are breast-feeding or not – the extra pounds gained during pregnancy slowly disappear in the year following childbirth. Some women do have to work at it by cutting out unnecessary snacks, adopting healthier eating habits and taking regular exercise.

Healthy eating and lifestyle advice for pregnancy is the same as that given in chapter 9 for the preconceptual period. You should also consider taking an essential fatty acid supplement (e.g. Efanatal, Milkarra in the UK; Neuromins in the US) specifically designed for women who are pregnant or breast feeding. These contain long chain polyunsaturated fatty acids important for your baby's brain development.

Exercise

Once pregnant, women are usually advised to reduce their level of exercise by around a third to 70 percent of what they were previously doing. A sensible level of exercise helps to improve your circulation so that more blood, oxygen and nutrients pass through the placenta to the baby. Exercise also helps to maintain stamina and fitness for the rigours of childbirth, and helps to strengthen abdominal muscles for pushing during labour.

The following guidelines should help you to develop a reasonable exercise regime:

- Don't let your pulse rise above 120 beats per minute.
- Don't let your body temperature rise above 37.8°C (100.04°F).
- Don't let yourself become dehydrated.

A professional on ...
Healthy eating in pregnancy

As a nutritionist, I am more involved than most people with the impact of food and nutrient balance on health, moods and energy levels – especially during pregnancy and for small children. Before my pregnancy, on the basis that to err is human and because my job is quite demanding, I experimented with many regimes. In the end, however, I tended to choose aspects of dietary modification that suited me most, leaving other desirable, but neglected, measures to tax my conscience.

However, when I discovered I was pregnant I decided to clean up my act. I followed all the standard advice i.e. no alcohol (especially in the first few months), no soft or blue cheeses, no liver, no undercooked eggs. I also took many steps that, as a nutritionist, I believed to be important, including: not eating foods with a potentially high allergy effect, such as peanuts, in case I set up an allergy in my developing child; making sure that I had sufficient essential fats in my diet from flax and other oils (good for brain development); and ensuring that I ate lots of fruit, vegetables, pulses and oily fish.

Despite my confidence that my approach was right, some things did not go according to plan. (Do they ever?) To my dismay, the only things that made me feel off colour were my daily vitamin and mineral supplements – and I tried different brands. This was a bit rich coming from someone who spent every day dishing out supplements to clients! Also, I neither like nor believe that a pregnant mother needs lots of dairy products as long as she is getting a varied diet with calcium-rich, green leafy vegetables. Still this caused a greater crisis of confidence than any other aspect – was I short-changing my child (and myself) by going against the standard advice? (As it turned out I had a satisfactory bone scan and my little boy remains free of all dairy allergy related problems). And, although I was unhappy about a high red-meat diet (because of the accumulation of pollutants in the animal's fat which could impact on a developing child and also because of the BSE crisis), I craved – very regularly – huge slabs of beef. I presume this must have been for the iron and zinc that meat provides.

Suzannah Olivier, nutritionist and author of *What Should I Feed My Baby?* (Weidenfeld & Nicolson)

A professional says ...

Ask questions! Never assume that your health caregiver has everything under control.

Marjorie Burke (Society For The Autistically Handicapped)

- Stop if you feel uncomfortable, faint, tired or are short of breath.
- Seek medical advice about whether you should continue exercising if you develop any complications linked with your pregnancy (e.g. vaginal bleeding, contractions, abdominal or chest pain).
- Do not use a jacuzzi as there are risks of overheating and of an air bubble (embolus) in the circulation
- Avoid water-skiing as water can be forced up into the vagina under pressure which may cause problems.

From the twentieth week of pregnancy onwards, it is wise to avoid high-impact sports such as jogging, sprinting or strenuous aerobics. From the fifth month of pregnancy, avoid abdominal exercises, as your stomach muscles are already stretched and further strain may do more harm than good. You should also avoid exercising on your back from this time as this can affect your circulation and cause dizziness. Skiing, horse-riding and other activities in which there is a risk of falling should also be avoided. Exercise classes especially designed for pregnant women are available in most towns and are also good for helping you to meet other women in the same position.

Towards the end of pregnancy, tiredness, bulkiness and the fact that the ligaments in the back and pelvis start to loosen will mean that your level of activity will reduce considerably (from around six months onwards).

Some women – for example those with a high risk of miscarriage, or who have high blood pressure – may be advised not to exercise during pregnancy at all. Always follow your obstetrician's advice.

Rest

Rest is important, too, for when you sit or lie down and relax, the blood flow through the placenta increases, so more oxygen and nutrients reach the baby. Research suggests that mothers who take part in prenatal relaxation classes, such as yoga, have fewer problems during pregnancy and have a lower risk of a low birth weight baby than mothers who do not relax regularly throughout pregnancy. It is therefore important to sit down for increasing periods of time as your pregnancy progresses. From around 30 weeks onwards, try to lie down for at least an hour mid-morning and mid-afternoon. Lying down relaxes the uterine muscles as well as boosting circulation through the placenta. Standing for long periods of time decreases blood flow to the uterus and is linked with low birth weight and pre-term delivery. The need for rest will also partly determine when women who work begin their maternity leave (see chapter 4).

Common pregnancy ailments

While you should not enter into pregnancy expecting problems, there are a few conditions that frequently occur. The most common of these include morning sickness, restless legs syndrome, constipation, piles, backache, varicose veins, blocked nose, indigestion, numbness and tingling in the hands, swollen ankles, vaginal thrush and night cramps. Common irritations also include not being able to reach down to clip your toenails, needing to be helped in and out of the bath and finding it difficult to get comfortable in bed so sleep is disturbed. While these are not serious, they can be a nuisance. Very often it is a case of forewarned is forearmed: for example, eating a higher fibre diet and drinking adequate amounts of fluid will help to avoid constipation. There are many books available on the subject and it is worth looking at a few of these so you are aware of the conditions that may arise during pregnancy.

Antenatal tests

Although every woman hopes to have a healthy, normal child, sadly around 1 in 650 babies is born with Down's syndrome and a similar number are born with major developmental abnormalities. Overall, one in every 20 babies is born with a congenital malformation although the vast majority are relatively minor. One of the decisions you will need to make when thinking about having a baby is the extent of antenatal testing you feel comfortable with – especially for those women aged over 35 or with a family history of congenital problems. While it is reassuring to know all tests are normal, some tests carry an increased risk of miscarriage, and there is no doubt that testing can cause a great deal of anxiety for some women.

A number of routine tests are performed on the first visit to the antenatal clinic, while others may be repeated at various times during pregnancy. Initial, one-off tests may include an external examination (to check your heart, lungs, breasts and abdomen to assess fitness and exclude unexpected findings such as a breast lump, ovarian cyst or uterine fibroid) and an internal examination

I decided to have my family in my early 30s, before I would need to think about amniocentesis – I didn't relish having a needle put through my abdomen into the womb and possibly harming my baby. Tina

I found the prospect of antenatal tests very comforting. I needed to know my baby did not have Down's syndrome, like his cousin. Anita

(performed only occasionally to confirm pregnancy or to check the pelvic organs). The internal examination is no longer routine and most doctors prefer not to do one just in case there is a miscarriage later which the woman may attribute to the examination (although this is unlikely).

Regular tests are usually performed at each antenatal clinic:

- Blood pressure is measured – if BP goes too high, it will affect blood circulation through the placenta and will need close monitoring and treatment. In later pregnancy, high blood pressure is one of the signs of pre-eclampsia (high blood pressure, protein loss in the urine and fluid retention) which may lead to fitting (eclampsia) if not treated.

- The height of the womb (fundus) in the abdomen is checked. This can be detected from around 12 weeks pregnancy, and helps to assess the pregnancy's progress. The length of pregnancy is approximately equal to the height of the uterus above the pubic bone measured in centimetres. A fundal height of 28cm (11in) is therefore approximately equivalent to 28 weeks pregnancy.

- The baby is gently examined through the abdominal wall to detect whether it is lying head first, in a breech position, and to exclude multiple pregnancy.

- The foetal heart is listened to; it can usually be heard from around 12 weeks. This is reassuring as it confirms the baby is well and, in later pregnancy, is an important sign of well-being.

- Urine is tested for protein (albuminuria) which may suggest a urinary tract infection or a problem with the kidneys. In later pregnancy it may be due to pre-eclampsia if there is also high blood pressure and fluid retention.

- Urine is tested for unexpected sugar (glycosuria) which suggests gestational diabetes. This affects 5 percent of non-diabetic women during pregnancy. A glucose tolerance test (GTT in which blood levels are measured after drinking a known amount of sugar in solution) will be offered to assess blood glucose levels if gestational diabetes is suspected.

- Urine is also tested for hidden blood (haematuria), white blood cells and/or nitrates which may suggest a urinary tract infection.

- Blood is taken for routine screening.

Routine blood tests

At your first visit to the antenatal clinic (usually at 8-12 weeks) routine blood tests are performed. These will be looking at:

- haemoglobin concentration to check for anaemia (usually repeated at least once around weeks 28-30 and when thought necessary)
- blood group (if the mother is Rhesus negative and her partner Rhesus positive, anti-Rhesus antibody levels will have to be checked regularly throughout pregnancy)
- syphilis screen
- blood glucose concentration (see under Urinalysis, page 160).

You will not be routinely checked for HIV during pregnancy, although in some areas anonymous blood samples are taken to assess the incidence of infection.

Blood tests for foetal abnormality

Maternal blood tests for foetal abnormality are offered routinely to pregnant women in some areas at 15 to 16 weeks, but only to those at increased risk (through age or family history) in others. The results vary depending on the mother's age and the length of pregnancy, and these factors have to be taken into account when assessing the outcome of the test. Different screening tests are available in different areas, and the most expensive may only be available privately.

- The alphafetoprotein (AFP) screens for spina bifida (high levels) and Down's syndrome (low levels). If the AFP is abnormal, a detailed ultrasound examination is offered. In the absence of any obvious foetal abnormality, a high AFP is linked with a 13-fold increase in risk of miscarriage, and a four times greater than normal risk of poor growth and stillbirth.
- The Triple Test measures levels of three different chemicals in the mother's blood (alphafetoprotein, unconjugated oestriol, human chorionic gonadotrophin). The detection rate for Down's syndrome is 66 percent. The Triple Plus Test also measures another factor (neutrophil alkaline phosphatase) which increases the detection rate for Down's syndrome to 70-80 percent.

I cried when I first saw my baby on the screen. I felt a sudden rush of love and felt this was when I really bonded with him as a person. He seemed to wave at me and then started turning somersaults as if showing off. I bought a photograph of the ultrasound – this is the first photo in our baby album. Tracy

After having my scan, I was sent to get my husband from the car park. The sight of two nurses rushing up to him with great excitement, grabbing him by both arms, sitting him down in a comfy chair and plying him with tea is one I shall never forget. 'Look – two heads,' they cried, holding up the pictures, 'it's twins!'. Elizabeth

- The Double Test measures the level of two different chemicals in the mother's blood (alphafetoprotein, free beta-HCG). The detection rate for Down's syndrome is 65-70 percent.
- The Quadruple Test measures the level of four chemicals in the mother's blood (alpha-HCG, free beta-HCG, alphafetoprotein, unconjugated oestriol). The detection rate for Down's syndrome is 75 percent.

If blood tests suggest a woman's risk of carrying a Down's syndrome baby is greater than one in 300 (5 percent of mothers tested) she will be offered a special ultrasound test (nuchal translucency ultrasound scan) and/or amniocentesis.

Ultrasound for foetal abnormality

Your first ultrasound scan (USS) is the first time you will see your baby and see him moving. It is a wonderful experience for most new parents.

The ultrasound is painless. Some warmed gel is placed on your abdomen and a probe is run up and down it. Inaudible, high-frequency sound waves pass through the abdomen and bounce back off different tissues to produce a signal which is converted into an image of your baby by a computer. There is no convincing evidence that ultrasound is harmful. The first ultrasound is increasingly carried out at the first antenatal appointment to confirm pregnancy and the number of babies, without having to do an internal examination.

You may be offered an ultrasound scan between 10 and 14 weeks if there is an increased risk of chromosomal or developmental abnormality due to maternal age or family history. This will help to detect major structural abnormalities such as spina bifida. Fluid at the back of the neck shows up as a black space known as the nuchal translucency. If this is thicker than normal, there is an increased risk of a chromosomal abnormality such as Down's syndrome.

For most women, the main ultrasound test to detect abnormalities is performed at 18-20 weeks. This locates the placenta and will also detect major developmental abnormalities such as spina bifida, cleft lip, cystic kidneys, abnormal brain or skeletal development. The overall detection rate for major structural abnormalities using ultrasound averages 76 percent. This unfortunately means that even when a mother is told her scan is normal there is still a 1 in 2,000 chance of an undiagnosed, major problem.

Despite common belief, a baby's sex cannot reliably be assessed on an ultrasound scan, as the female foetus has swollen genitals during early development that often resemble a scrotum on ultrasound. While the scan can give a good indication of sex, it is important not to rely on this, just in case.

> One of the many issues that I have had to consider as an older woman (aged 44) trying to get pregnant is the increased risk that I might have a child with some form of disability. My youngest brother has a moderate learning difficulty and I work with people who have a range of physical and learning disabilities. Unfortunately my experience has not really helped me clarify my feelings about raising a child with a disability. On the one hand I am committed to empowering disabled people to lead a full and productive life. On the other hand I have no illusions about the impact this would have on my family and myself and I would have to consider the future care of my child when I would no longer be able to look after her or him. There is no easy answer to the dilemma about testing and making the decision whether or not to continue with a high-risk pregnancy. If I do become pregnant I will have to make the decision that feels right for me at the time. Bernadette

Tests that analyse foetal cells

If your risk of a chromosomal abnormality is assessed at greater than 1 in 300 because of your age, family history or the results of ultrasound or blood tests, you will be offered a more invasive test to check the health of your baby.

Cells from your developing baby can be analysed to predict accurately chromosomal abnormalities such as Down's syndrome in which there is an extra chromosome (Trisomy 21). Chromosome analysis will also accurately tell you the sex of your baby, and this can help predict inherited genetic disorders that are linked to a baby's sex such as haemophilia or Duchenne's muscular dystrophy, both of which are more common in males. Genetic counselling will help you decide which antenatal tests are right for your particular situation once you decide to start a family. A number of different tests are available, all of which carry around a 1 percent risk of miscarriage. The risks and benefits of the procedure will be thoroughly explained to you before you decide whether or not to go ahead.

Chorionic villus sampling (CVS)

This involves passing a fine needle into the placenta under ultrasound control to obtain a small tissue biopsy. CVS is usually performed between 11 and 14 weeks.

Amniocentesis

This involves passing a fine needle through the abdominal wall and into the amniotic fluid under local anaesthetic. The needle is guided into the amniotic space under ultrasound control and a small sample of fluid is withdrawn. The fluid contains shed cells from your baby whose chromosomes can be checked. Amniocentesis is only usually performed after 16 weeks.

Cordocentesis

This is a new technique which involves taking a sample of baby's blood from the umbilical cord. A thin needle is inserted into the womb under local anaesthetic and using ultrasound to locate the cord.

Sex in pregnancy

A woman's sex drive can go up, down or remain the same during pregnancy – every woman, and every pregnancy is different. When a low sex drive does occur, it is often linked with tiredness, especially during the first three months of pregnancy, and again during the last three months when you are carrying around extra weight, getting up at night to pass water and finding it less easy to sleep. The last three months of pregnancy are also the time when your levels of the milk hormone, prolactin, are starting to rise. Prolactin has a powerful effect in damping down sex drive, so it is perfectly normal to go off sex in late pregnancy and during the first few months of breast-feeding. Having said that high levels of other hormones (oestrogen and progesterone) can cancel out the effects of prolactin.

Some women find their sex drive increases during pregnancy in response to their changing hormones, especially in the middle three months of pregnancy. Increased blood flow to the genitals can also make them feel sexier as a result of engorgement and increased vaginal lubrication. Many women also find their orgasms improve during pregnancy – again, especially during the middle three months. Orgasm may become easier to achieve and more intense. Some women find they become multiorgasmic for the first time. This again is linked with hormone changes, increased blood flow to the vagina and clitoris, increased skin sensitivity (in response to the oestrogen hormone) and increased vaginal lubrication. Psychologically, you may also be feeling closer to your partner as having a baby draws you together. This can make sex a more loving and fulfilling experience – and partners also tend to be increasingly loving and attentive.

Sex and miscarriage

Many couples worry that sex can harm their baby or increase the risk of miscarriage. In a healthy pregnancy, where there are no complications, a normal sex life can be enjoyed without fear of causing a miscarriage. Some women, however, may be advised by their doctors to avoid sex during the first three months as a precaution – especially if they notice any bleeding or staining, have low abdominal cramps, ruptured membranes or a history of recurrent miscarriage. In later pregnancy, the contractions linked with orgasm have been shown to slow the baby's heart momentarily but this is not harmful as long as the baby's blood supply is normal. For women whose placenta is not working as well as it should, or for those who have high blood pressure, it may be advisable to avoid orgasm during the last three months.

Unless you have been specifically advised not to make love, you can carry on as normal, although it is important to be extra gentle. If sex hurts, or you notice blood loss or pain, stop and seek advice from your midwife or doctor. Oral sex (cunnilingus) is potentially harmful as, in rare cases, air has been blown into the vagina and managed to enter the bloodstream through the spongy lining of the pregnant womb. Oral sex should therefore be avoided by pregnant women.

Sex and infection

It was once thought that sex during pregnancy might increase the risk of a womb infection, but this is no longer thought to be the case as long as the membranes have not ruptured. It is still possible to catch sexually transmissible diseases during pregnancy however, and if you are at risk of these you should continue with safer sex practices and always use a condom. Your immune system changes during pregnancy so you are more likely to get thrush which can sometimes be passed on sexually. Your ability to fight off genital warts is also reduced and some women develop large warts during pregnancy as a result (see chapter 8). One of the most important infections to be aware of is genital herpes, which causes recurrent, painful ulcers. If you think you may have genital herpes it is vital to tell your doctor and midwife: if the virus is active during labour you may be advised to have a Caesarean to help protect the baby from infection. If you are worried that you might have an infection, always seek medical advice.

Sex and childbirth

Whether or not sex can trigger labour in a healthy pregnancy is still uncertain. It may play a role in late pregnancy in women who have had previous premature deliveries. Increased levels of a hormone, oxytocin, do occur during orgasm and this can cause powerful contraction of the uterus. It is also possible that hormone-like substances (prostaglandins) in semen can help to ripen the cervix and trigger labour in late pregnancy – these prostaglandins are similar to those used to induce delivery in hospital. As the time for childbirth approaches, many women make love in a deliberate attempt to hurry the baby along – and it does seem to work in some cases. Research suggests that making love with the woman on top or in a side-to-side position does not stimulate labour, but the classic missionary position (man on top) may increase the risk of premature labour.

In the final three months of pregnancy, the missionary position becomes almost impossible however, as the bump gets in the way, and the mother finds it uncomfortable lying on her back. Once the baby's head engages, there is also very little room in the vagina. A side-by-side position or a sitting position is usually best. Another popular position is with the woman lying, crouching or kneeling with her back to her partner so he enters her vagina from behind. This means the uterus is free of pressure. She can then also use her buttock muscles to help grip the penis and control penetration.

Prenatal stimulation

There is increasing evidence that providing your baby with an enriched environment in the womb helps to stimulate foetal brain development and enhance your baby's creativity and ability to learn. A prenatal stimulation programme (e.g. talking to your baby, singing to it, or reading stories) is usually started around 20-24 weeks[4].

Your rights during pregnancy

During pregnancy, you have the right to reasonable time off from work for attending antenatal appointments, parentcraft and relaxation classes. Time off should be paid at your usual rate, although your employer will usually need a medical certificate confirming your pregnancy and expected date of confinement.

You are entitled to work conditions that are safe for you and your baby, including reasonable facilities to rest when necessary, and to maternity leave.

If you find difficulty attending your antenatal appointments, receiving payment while attending them or feel your employment has been unfairly terminated because of your pregnancy, you have the right to seek redress from an Industrial Tribunal.

For more information on work and your legal rights during pregnancy, see chapters 4 and 7.

Illness during pregnancy

When thinking about having a baby, few women think of the potential risks to their own health. Pregnancy is a natural state, and the majority of women having babies do so with no long-term serious effects. Some pregnancy-associated conditions can put a mother's health at risk however, even if only temporarily. These include ectopic pregnancy, blood clotting disorders, pregnancy-induced high blood pressure and gestational diabetes. While it is important not to dwell on possible negative outcomes, it is equally important to attend clinics regularly for antenatal screening (designed to detect problems as early as possible) and to report unusual symptoms such as pain, bleeding, fainting or collapse to your healthcare professionals immediately.

---

4 For more on prenatal stimulation see Dr Sarah Brewer *Superbaby* (Thorsons).

Chapter 11:
Options for Birth

We were planning to emigrate to Africa within a few years to be near my husband's family. When talking to my doctor, I suddenly realized I had no idea what standard of obstetric care to expect. I've never been a follower of the natural birth movement – all that huffing, puffing and unnecessary pain. I wanted painkillers and plenty of them! This brought my plans to have babies forward as I realized I wanted to have them in this country. Joan

Even if having a baby is still a moot subject it is useful to form some advance ideas on the type of birth you might prefer, as this may have a bearing on when – or where – you decide to conceive.

I was booked into a small local hospital for my first baby. No one warned me there was only one anaesthetist on call at night – for the whole hospital, not just the delivery suite. When I asked for epidural pain relief, I was told the anaesthetist was tied up in an emergency and unavailable. By the time he came to see me it was too late – I was virtually fully dilated and he wouldn't do it. I'm now expecting my second child and have insisted on being referred to a teaching hospital 40 miles away. Pattie

There are a number of options to consider including whether you want to:

- give birth at home, in hospital or at a community or GP midwife unit (if available)
- have NHS or private obstetric care
- be delivered by a hospital doctor, GP or midwife
- be delivered by a midwife you know from a local team, or are happy for anyone on duty at the time to attend to you
- stay in hospital afterwards and for how long.

Home births

Home births are becoming increasingly popular but are not always easy to arrange – few GPs have much experience in delivering babies now. Having said that, you do have a legal right to give birth at home should you wish to (even for a first child) and the local health authority are obliged to provide a qualified attendant. If you want a home birth, your doctor should be willing to refer you to a midwife experienced in carrying out home birth. If you encounter difficulty in being referred to one, you can always contact the midwifery unit at your local hospital and ask for advice. You also have the choice of registering for maternity care with another local GP rather than your usual family doctor if you wish, providing the new doctor is willing to take you on for maternity care alone.

Other options

DOMINO
The DOMINO scheme (which stands for domiciliary, in and out) is one in which the midwife comes to you when labour starts and then goes to hospital with you to deliver your baby. You can then go home again – assuming all is well with you and the baby – within a few hours of birth.

One-to-One
Some hospitals are pioneering a One-to-One approach in which a named midwife provides most of the care for a particular expectant mother. Whenever possible, the named midwife provides both antenatal and delivery care although the woman also gets to know a named back-up in case the first midwife is unavailable when needed. Women using the One-to-One scheme appreciate the continuity of care and are more positive and confident about giving birth. They tend to have a shorter stay in hospital, and are more likely to succeed in breast-feeding than those receiving traditional care.

Which hospital?

Ask around about the different hospitals available to you, and which are the most friendly, flexible and helpful. Some hospitals have birthing stools, facilities for water birth, 24-hour obstetric anaesthetists and a relaxed approach to eating during labour, for example. Others are more inflexible and it is useful to be aware of these in advance. There is considerable variation in facilities and attitudes in different parts of the country. You can get information on local facilities by contacting your Community Health Council.

I chose to have a home birth for my first child, despite the opposition of my GP. I looked round the hospital birthing rooms and found the equipment and sterile atmosphere daunting. I wanted my baby in the comfort and reassuring familiarity of my own home, where no strangers could steal her from under my nose. In the end, I registered for maternity care with another local GP who was willing to support my wishes.

Jane

My partner is a very controlled person and I didn't want him to witness my possible loss of control during birth. He was quite happy not to be present and my mother provided moral support and back-rubs instead. Rhona

I was present at the birth of both my children. These were the most moving experiences of my life. Paul

Keeping an open mind

With all of the above in mind, it is important to remain flexible in your wishes. Different women have different needs during pregnancy and it is not always possible to tell what these will be in advance. Even the best-laid plans may have to be abandoned in the face of particular circumstances or complications at the time of delivery. A woman may then feel her birth experience was not as fulfilling as she would have wished. If you have your heart set on a natural delivery, then need a forceps delivery or Caesarean, it is easy to feel you have somehow failed because you have lost control.

I was determined to have a natural delivery with no drugs, and to spend labour in a birthing pool. In the end, my labour was induced early and the pains were worse than I expected. I had pethidine and felt really uptight about giving in to drugs. After several hours of failure to progress, I realized I had to accept the offer of an epidural. After my baby was born, I felt a complete failure even though I managed to push him out myself. It took months to come to terms with the fact that delivering a healthy baby was in fact one of the greatest successes of my life. Next time round, I won't form any firm opinions but will play it as it goes. Annie

I knew from the beginning that I would probably need a Caesarean as I had recurrent genital herpes virtually all the time during pregnancy. In many ways, this was a comfort as I knew how and when my baby would be born. One of my friends who also had a Caesarean felt she had let her baby down by not having a natural delivery. I could never see the sense in that. She carried the baby for nine months and brought him safely into the world. What does it matter which method was used? Rena

Birth attendant/s

You will also need to think about who you want to attend the birth – while this is usually a partner, some mothers-to-be prefer to have their own mother, sister or best friend with them for support instead.

Most hospital delivery suites limit the number of attendants you are allowed to have in with you to one or two, so check beforehand if you wish to have more than one person with you.

The Active Birth Movement
by **Janet Balaskas**

The Active Birth movement was founded in the late 1970s when women began to use upright positions and remained mobile during labour instead of lying or semi-reclining in bed. The approach is practical with the emphasis on preparation of both body and mind as well as on-going emotional support throughout pregnancy.

Pregnant women are encouraged to join active birth classses as early as possible, although it is never too late to join. You will be invited to attend a weekly class of easy 'gravitational' yoga which is non-strenuous, can be done without previous experience, and is ideally suited for pregnancy. These yoga-based exercises help to relieve tightness and tension in the body, improve flexibility, encourage good breathing and circulation. They also relieve many of the common complaints of pregnancy such as backache or cramps, and are emotionally supportive and deeply relaxing.

Besides helping to make pregnancy more healthy and enjoyable, these classes offer effective practical preparation for labour and birth. Women are taught how to be comfortable in upright positions and to manage pain in labour with breathing and relaxation. There are also informative courses or workshops which aim to increase the potential for a natural birth and breast-feeding, while introducing expectant parents to a wide range of birth options. They have an open-minded approach, covering the same ground as traditional antenatal classes, with an additional emphasis on upright labour and birth positions, relaxation, breathing and the use of warm water during labour and possibly also for birth.

After the birth, Active Birth teachers offer ongoing support in the form of postnatal yoga classes in which women meet up with mums from their pregnancy class. Many include baby massage which may help to relieve colic and fretfulness and encourage babies to sleep better. The Active Birth Centre also offers a water birth pool hire service.

Janet Balaskas is the movement's founder and Director of the Active Birth Centre in London (see Resources, page 235). She is also author of *Active Birth* (Thorsons).

While in America I heard about the trend of having a 'doula' as birth attendant. A doula is essentially an experienced mother who stays with you at birth and provides emotional support. They have caught on because in many large hospitals, midwives have largely been replaced by obstetricians for medico-legal reasons. I liked the idea and invited my mother, mother-in-law and older sister (mother of three) to attend the birth of my second child at home. Lee

Pain relief

While it may seem premature to be thinking about pain relief options, it is useful and reassuring to be aware of the range of methods available.

Natural pain relief methods include:

- relaxation and breathing techniques
- acupuncture
- aromatherapy
- autogenic training
- homeopathy
- self-hypnosis
- water birth
- massage
- reflexology
- TENS (transcutaneous electrical nerve stimulation).

Drugs for pain relief include:

- nitrous oxide and oxygen (Entonox or 'gas and air')
- pethidine
- meptazinol
- epidural (conventional and mobile types)
- spinal block
- other local anaesthetic injections (paracervical and pudendal blocks)
- general anaesthetic.

Birth plans

Over 70 percent of pregnant women now make a birth plan. This is given to the midwife who oversees the birth and documents the expectant mother's feelings on a number of issues, such as who should (or should not) attend her birth, whether she wishes a mobile or active birth, what pain relief she desires, whether or not the placenta should be actively removed or left to be expelled on its own, and their wishes regarding episiotomy. The plan helps to improve communication between mother and birth carers, at a time when she is vulnerable and wants to feel more in control. Researching and preparing a birth plan during pregnancy helps them to absorb information, and this is important in reducing negative feelings about pregnancy and in allaying depression after the birth. The National Childbirth Trust provides a series of leaflets, including one called 'Making a Birth Plan' (sponsored by Tesco supermarkets). This suggests that a birth plan should be written around the 36th week of pregnancy, although it is often helpful to start thinking about it and discussing it from 28 weeks onwards.

In a controversial Court of Appeal decision in 1998, it was established that a pregnant woman cannot be forced to have a Caesarean even if her baby's life is at stake. The mother's right to choose how she is treated during delivery therefore outweighs the rights of her unborn child.

What does giving birth feel like?

The question most on the minds of women thinking about having their first baby is, 'What does it feel like to give birth?' Different women have different birth experiences. Try not to dwell on the horror stories that many women tell with relish. Ask people you know and whose opinions you trust, such as relatives, close friends and familiar healthcare professionals.

It is important to read about labour and childbirth so that you are fully aware of what is happening at each stage of the process. Lack of knowledge increases anxiety and fear and these in turn increase your sensitivity to pain. One of the strongest factors in keeping pain at bay is confidence and relaxation.

There are three main stages in the birthing process:

- **Stage 1:** the waters break and regular contractions push the baby down against the cervix so it slowly widens to a diameter of 10cm (4in).
- **Stage 2:** the womb continues to contract and the baby passes down the birth canal to be born – usually head first. The umbilical cord is then cut.
- **Stage 3:** the placenta (afterbirth) is delivered.

Stage 1

The pains at the onset of labour may be felt in the lower back, pelvis, front of the abdomen or even at the tops of the legs.

> **The start of labour felt like a really bad period with heavy dragging pains in my lower back.** Pridha

> If the pain of childbirth was really that bad, we wouldn't have a population explosion, would we? Few women would be prepared to have another child. I find the fact that the average number of children per family is 2.4 very reassuring although I haven't had a baby yet. Nuala

I was in labour for six hours without feeling a thing – I watched huge contractions sweep past the monitor and the midwife couldn't believe I felt nothing at all. I put it down to the raspberry leaf tablets I took during the last 8 weeks. Helen

The pain was a regular stab with slicing pains in between. Joanna

Although the pain is bad when it is there, it comes and goes in waves. That's what makes it easy to cope with. You have regular breathing spaces before it slowly builds up again. The peak of pain only lasts a few seconds before fading away. Katy

The pain felt like bad wind which I couldn't shift. Olga

Before my water broke the pain was gentle and distant. Once the waters broke, all hell was let loose so to speak. The pain instantly became ten times worse. Monique

Descriptions of the type of pain experienced range from 'hardly anything at all' to 'the worst pain of my life' which is not very helpful when you are wondering how childbirth will affect you. Many women admit that the pain is unpleasant, but somehow find it a 'worthwhile' or 'natural' pain that they can cope with better than other pains they have undergone.

I wish someone had warned me first time round how much childbirth was going to hurt – I would then have requested an epidural rather than going through agony. I made sure I had an epidural with my next two. Elizabeth

Given the choice between childbirth and taking my driving test, I'd choose having a baby every time. I've never understood why some women make such a fuss about it. It's not really a pain at all, more a sensation that you can easily distance yourself from. Just concentrate on the baby – that has to be your main priority. Any pain is secondary. Breathing exercises helped me focus in on my baby. Sue

The time between the end of stage 1 (dilation of the cervix) and the start of stage 2 (pushing your baby out) is known as transition. For some women it only lasts momentarily, for others contractions stop for 20 minutes or more. Transition is a strange experience for some women, in which they develop shakes, feel cold or nauseated, irritable, weepy, angry and bad-tempered. Others become uncharacteristically abusive until they develop the urge to push.

I hated transition. It made me feel helpless, irritable. I screamed at my husband and became quite irrational. I just wanted it all to end. Gopa

Stage 2

Labour pains take on a different quality during the second stage of labour, in which you push your baby out.

The pains stopped after I was fully dilated. In their place was a strange stretching, splitting and slithery feeling – I though I was going to burst. Vladya

My husband used to joke that giving birth must feel like taking your bottom lip and trying to stretch it over a ten-pin bowling ball. He was right. Nicki

Giving birth itself was a burning, stinging, tearing sensation rather than the stabbing, slicing and kicking pains of labour. It's strange though. You can't really remember it afterwards – there are so many hormones and emotions around to dull the memory. Lucy

Once I got the urge to push, time seemed to fly – my body was working on instinct and everything happened so quickly. The sensation of my baby's head coming down was incredible – quite exhilarating and primeval. I realized I was making a lot of grunting noises – not because I hurt, but because it helped me to push – like trying to deliver a giant constipated turd. Apparently grunting is quite normal. Julie

I didn't feel a thing throughout as I had an epidural with regular top-ups. I listened to classical music and my body just pushed my baby out with very little effort from me. Jilly

My first baby was born within three hours of my first contraction. I wanted to push by the time I got to the hospital and he just seemed to pop out. I only just got to the maternity ward in time. Freemal

The birth of my second baby was so traumatic, I found I had no feelings for her for several months –it was very difficult to bond. Annie

Whatever you go through during delivery, as soon as you see and hold your baby for the first time, everything else is forgotten. I felt so proud and full of love, I wanted to have another baby straight away, and said so. My husband visibly paled. Sal

The birth was the greatest event in my life. The doctor who delivered the twins said: 'This will be the hardest work you've ever done in your life – and the most rewarding. I know, I've been there.' She was right, and the sense of achievement, of joy, of wonder ... unforgettable. If I close my eyes, I can be there now. What a privilege to have even one such experience. Elizabeth

Stage 3

There are two methods of delivering the placenta:

In the 'managed' third stage, you are given an injection (syntometrine) in your thigh as soon as your baby's shoulders are born. This helps your uterus to contract strongly and both reduces the risk of haemorrhage and eases expulsion of the placenta. After delivery, the umbilical cord is then cut and the midwife delivers the placenta around five minutes later by pulling on the umbilical cord.

In a 'natural' third stage of labour, the umbilical cord is not cut after birth. Instead, the baby is put to the breast and encouraged to suckle. Breast-feeding stimulates secretion of a hormone (oxytocin) which causes the womb to contract. The midwife then waits until the placenta naturally separates from the uterus which may be ten to 90 minutes later.

The way the third stage of delivery is managed is one of the things you may wish to discuss with your midwife and include in your birth plan. You can only have a natural third stage if you have had a natural labour, without drugs or epidural.

My placenta failed to come out so I had to have a general anaesthetic and a scrape. This was such a shame as I'd done so well up till then. I made my husband promise to stay with the baby the whole time I was away in theatre so we weren't given the wrong one back by mistake. Joanna

Recording the birth

Some parents decide to film the birth of their baby. This is something you need to think through in advance and to feel comfortable about.

I'm a video-bore. It's so much nicer than being a photo-bore ... there's no escape, and they go on for hours and hours. My wife flatly refused to allow me to bring a video camera anywhere near her when our children were born. But I was able to sneak one in afterwards ... and it was worth it. The stories that lose something in the retelling and end with a tame, 'You should have been there ...' retain their charm on video. The pictures of my son Ben giving his younger brother a packet of biscuits on his 0th birthday are as funny today as they were then. If only I'd had the discipline to switch the camera off at that point – the other eight hours never get the same enthusiastic response! John

Breast-feeding

The ideal way to feed your baby is as nature intended, with breast milk. To women who do choose this option, new government guidelines recommend putting their baby to the breast within an hour of birth.

For me, breast-feeding was the most satisfying experience about being a mother. Putting my baby to the breast immediately after birth and realizing she could latch on and suckle instinctively was just magic.

For more information on breast-feeding, see chapter 12.

Gay parenting: Options for birth
by **Lisa Saffron**

Margaret, a 30-year-old lesbian mother, rated her experience of childbirth within the NHS highly:

When I was in labour, we were completely open about the fact that I was a lesbian. The two midwives who delivered Leah were lesbians and that made it extra special. My partner, Cecilia, cut the cord. I felt supported throughout the labour and delivery, like I was being looked after by my sisters. It was a great experience.

Jude, lesbian mother of two daughters:

For the most part, everyone I had contact with (during antenatal care, labour and delivery) whether or not they knew I was lesbian and had done self-insemination, was positive in every respect that I can imagine. I decided that I would neither stay in the closet nor wear a big 'L' on my forehead. If my lesbianism was an issue, we would talk about it. If it wasn't, then it wouldn't matter. That's why, in some cases, the midwives didn't know and it's not on my forms and that's fine. But I thought it was important for the midwives I saw all the time and who I thought might deliver Jordan to know, specifically because of Donna, my partner. If I had been on my own, it might not have mattered quite as much but because Donna is such an important part of my life, I wanted them to know. She wasn't just a birth partner. She is my partner. She was there not just in the capacity of wiping my brow while I was having contractions but as part of Jordan's life.

Chapter 12:
The Early Days

After months of planning, preparation and excitement, your baby will eventually arrive and your life will change beyond all recognition as you adjust to being a parent. Rather than only having to consider yourself and your partner, you now have to factor in the needs of another vulnerable and totally dependent individual.

New mothers should plan to have sufficient help at home to keep things running smoothly during the first few days and preferably several weeks, while they recover from the rigours of pregnancy and birth (see chapter 5).

Often, new fathers feel left out when their partners stay in hospital for a few days and are shown how to care for the baby. It is a good idea for women to show their partners all the tips and tricks they are taught – how to hold the baby, bathe him and change him – so they feel involved. This also makes it more likely that he'll share the tasks when they get home. It is also important that both new parents continue showing affection to each other – some fathers feel left out when the new baby seems to be the focus of its mother's attention.

Should you sleep with your baby?

In many parts of the world, newborn babies spend the whole time with their mother, sleeping with her at night and strapped to her by day. Increasing numbers of Western parents are also choosing to sleep with their baby. This early closeness is important for a baby's sense of security. Sleeping with your baby seems to be safe as long as neither parent smokes, and neither has been drinking alcohol or taking drugs that affect consciousness (e.g. sleeping tablets). There is some evidence that having the baby sleep in the same room as an adult may even reduce the risk of sudden infant death syndrome.

Having your baby in bed with you means it is easier to breast-feed on demand – all you have to do is roll on your side and offer the breast to the hungry infant – you can then doze lightly while feeding at the same time. One of the most civilized ways to do this is with the Bed-Side-Bed – a special three-sided cot that fits next to your bed and which can be adjusted to the same height as your mattress. This virtually brings your baby into bed with you, but allows you all to have your own space. Once the baby is older a fourth side can be fitted to convert it into a standard cot. Later, both sides can be removed to make a small first-size bed, or one side can be removed and the base lowered to make a small child-sized sofa.

> It seemed insane to banish a vulnerable new baby to his own room – surely guaranteed to cause a fit of screaming when he woke and found himself alone. New babies need constant love, cuddles and security. We found the Bed-Side-Bed invaluable. Our baby was virtually sleeping in bed with us, but had his own sleeping area to one side. I was confident I couldn't roll on to him in my sleep, and he couldn't roll out of bed either. It was brilliant for breast-feeding, too. Sarah

A professional on ...
Support for a good start

I thought I knew all about being tired. I had worked as a children's houseman in a ward full of seriously ill babies and children. Some nights, I never went to bed at all, and worked all next day, and the next. But none of this prepared me for how utterly exhausted staying at home with my own newborn baby could make me.

My message to anyone who is planning to have a baby is to accept all the help that is offered, particularly during the few weeks after the birth when you and your baby are getting to know each other. And if adequate help is not offered, do your level best to find some.

Changing hormones, changed routines, the unfamiliar and sometimes challenging demands of a newborn baby can all add up to total exhaustion, particularly if a succession of sleepless nights are thrown in for good measure. Feeling worn out can happen to anyone. It's not a sign that you're suddenly cracking up.

Of course you need to become self-confident and independent in the long run about looking after your baby but, if you have managed life well in your pre-baby days, there is no reason why you should not be equally successful with your new responsibilities, and enjoy them.

However, getting into the rhythm of things takes time. You have to rebalance your life to accommodate what will undoubtedly be a demanding new personality who does not hesitate to make his or her wants known. Involve your partner in your baby's care, and don't be ashamed to accept as much help as is offered from your family, particularly from your mother.

This is a time when the mothers of new mothers come into their own, not just in the usual ways, but as a powerful shield against the misery of postnatal depression. Medical research has shown that the support of a caring mother is one of the best safeguards against postnatal depression that you can have.

Dr Ann Whitehead, GP

A professional on ...
Reducing the risk of cot death: start thinking now

Although cot death is rare, it is still something that every prospective parent needs to think about, and if you want to reduce the chances of it happening you have to act from as early as the moment you plan your pregnancy.

What is cot death?

Cot death is the sudden unexpected death of a baby for no obvious reason. The post mortem examination may explain some deaths but those that remain unexplained are registered as sudden infant death syndrome or sudden unexpected deaths in infancy, more commonly known as cot death.

Nearly ten babies die each week of cot death in the UK; that's more than the number dying from meningitis, leukaemia or road traffic accidents. But no one knows what causes cot death, and researchers think it unlikely to be attributable to one single cause. It is probably associated with a number of different factors, affecting a baby when they are at a vulnerable stage in their development.

Will your baby be at risk?

We do know that some babies are more at risk – those from a multiple birth or who are premature, and babies whose mothers smoked during pregnancy, for example. But until we know what actually causes cot death we cannot find 'the cure' and until that day every parent and prospective parent should do all they can to reduce the chances of it happening.

To help reduce the risk of cot death happening to your future baby there are six simple steps you should follow from conception until your baby is at least a year old or more:

- *Quit smoking in pregnancy – fathers too:* smoking in pregnancy increases the risk of cot death, so you have to think about quitting while you're planning your pregnancy. To give your baby the best chance then try to give up sooner rather than later. Fathers should give up too, as pregnant woman find it harder to quit if their partners continue smoking. It is best not to smoke at all, but if you can't give up, the less you smoke the more you lower the risk (see p. 119).

- *Place your baby on its back to sleep:* the risk of cot death is reduced if babies are not put on their tummies to sleep. Start putting the baby on its back from when they're born, as babies who learn to back-sleep early on are the most likely to settle in that position. Side-sleeping is not as safe as sleeping on the back. Healthy babies placed on their backs are not more likely to choke, and research has shown that they often suffer less from many common childhood complaints such as earache and coughs.

- *Do not let anyone smoke in the same room as your baby:* babies exposed to cigarette smoke after birth are also at an increased risk of cot death. It is best if nobody smokes in the house. You should hold firm if visitors try to smoke indoors, and ask them to smoke outside. It follows that you shouldn't take babies into smoky places.

  If you smoke, sharing a bed with your baby may increase the risk of cot death even if you do not smoke in bed.

- *Do not let your baby get too hot:* overheating can increase the risk of cot death. Babies can overheat because of too much bedding or clothing, or because the room is too hot. Duvets or quilts, baby nests, sheepskins, wedges, bedding rolls, cot bumpers and pillows may carry a risk of overheating, so strike them off your shopping list now. Buy sheets and lightweight blankets instead as these can be more easily regulated if your baby feels too hot.

  When you check your baby, if he or she is sweating or their tummy feels hot to touch, take off some of the bedding. Don't worry if the baby's hands or feet feel cool – this is normal. Babies do not need hot rooms; all-night heating is rarely necessary. Keep the room at about 18°C (65°F). Babies should never sleep with a hot water bottle or electric blanket, next to a radiator, heater or fire, or in direct sunshine.

- *Keep your baby's head uncovered – place your baby in the 'feet to foot' position:* babies whose heads are covered accidentally with bedding are at an increased risk of cot death. To prevent babies wriggling down under the covers place their feet at the foot of the cot and make the bed up so that the covers reach no higher than the shoulders. You should tuck the covers securely so they cannot slip over your baby's head.

- *If your baby is unwell, seek medical advice promptly:* babies often have minor illnesses which you do not need to worry about. Make sure your baby drinks plenty of fluids and is not too hot. If your baby is ill they may need fewer, not more, blankets.

If your baby sleeps a lot, wake him or her regularly for a drink. It may, however, be difficult to judge whether an illness is more serious requiring prompt medical attention, particularly if this is your first baby and you are not used to caring for children. The following guidelines may help you.

You should seek medical advice early and quickly if your baby:

- has a high pitched or weak cry, is less responsive, is much less active or more floppy than usual
- looks very pale all over, grunts with each breath, has obvious dips in the upper tummy or between the ribs as he or she breaths
- takes less than a third of usual fluids, passes much less urine than usual, vomits green fluid, or passes blood in motions
- has a high fever with sweating.

Dial 999 and ask for an ambulance if your baby:

- stops breathing or goes blue
- is unresponsive and shows no awareness of what is going on
- has glazed eyes and does not focus on anything

- cannot be woken
- has a fit.

Every parent's nightmare

If a baby dies the Foundation for the Study of Infant Deaths (FSID) can offer bereaved families support. Telephone the 24-hour helpline (0171 235 1721) for more details. Specially trained advisors staff the helpline, and calls are always answered personally, 24 hours a day, all year round.

The helpline staff will be able to help by:

- giving you information and support as well as a listening ear
- sending you a telephone chargecard so you can call the helpline free of charge
- putting you in touch with one of FSID's 'befrienders' – somebody who lives near you and has experienced the loss of a baby. You do not have to get in touch with the befriender straight away but keep their number for a time when you need their support.

Particularly, you may be interested in receiving a copy of FSID's booklet 'When a baby dies suddenly and unexpectedly'. This booklet helps to explain what happens after a baby dies and also the feelings and emotions that you may experience. Telephone FSID's 24-hour helpline for a copy.

Help is at hand so enjoy planning for your baby

Remember that cot death is rare. Research is continuing to help us understand more about cot death, and since 1991, when the reduce-the-risk message was introduced, the number of babies dying has more than halved. So please don't let the worry of cot death stop you from enjoying your pregnancy and your baby's first few months.

Copies of the reduce-the-risk leaflet, produced jointly by FSID and the Department of Health, can be obtained by calling 0800 555 777.

Samantha Sherratt, Information and Media Manager at the FSID

I breast-fed my baby for nine months. I worked full-time from home, so it was a simple matter for my mother to bring the baby through for a feed when he was hungry. I had to go to London once a week on business. This entailed building up a stock of expressed milk in the freezer for use while I was away. I took a breast pump and cool bag with me and nipped into the toilets to express when necessary. I kept the milk chilled and froze it when I got home to replace that used during the day. Sarah

Breast-feeding

Every women who is planning to have a baby should read *Breast is Best* by Drs Penny and Andrew Stanway (Pan) for a complete picture of breast-feeding, including why it is by far the healthiest option for both mother and baby, hints and tips on how to get started, how to do it successfully – even when working – and how to overcome problems.

Breast milk is the most nutritionally complete food you can offer your infant for both his physical and mental development. It contains:

- all the energy, protein, fat, sugar, vitamins, minerals and fluids your baby needs for his first six months
- antibodies to protect against disease
- active scavenger immune cells to protect against disease
- natural antibacterial and antiviral substances
- essential fatty acids that are vital for development of your baby's brain
- growth factors that influence your baby's growth and maturation.

The best way to breast-feed is to supply your baby with milk whenever he needs it, otherwise known as 'on demand'. Ideally, your baby should be breast-fed exclusively for four to six months and should still be given breast milk after weaning on to solids, up until at least his first birthday. Many children continue to enjoy the benefits of breast-feeding until the age of two years or beyond.

While pregnant and breast-feeding, consider taking essential fatty acid supplements containing long-chain fatty acids (e.g. Efanatal, Milkarra in the UK; Neuromins in the US) designed to enhance the amount of essential fatty acids – essential for brain development – your baby receives.

Breast-feeding and returning to work

Some mothers decide the logistics of breast-feeding are too difficult once the time comes to return to work. While returning to work and continuing to breast-feed requires good organizational skills, it can be done.

Although there is no legal obligation to do so, many employers provide a safe and healthy place for workers who are breast-feeding to express and store milk, including a fridge. Regulations do require that women who are pregnant or breast-feeding have a suitable place to rest, however, even if they have to take their own cool box and ice-packs into work with them.

> Determined to breast-feed for at least three months (and driven by guilt at leaving my new baby), I have managed to express breast milk in the middle of an open-plan office surrounded by men. I'm not sure who was most embarrassed by the gentle thrub of the electric motor (forget hand pumps and gentle milking techniques, the powerful suction of a pump can get it all out within minutes, with only the occasional conversation-stopping 'ssshhluuurp' as the vacuum seal is broken). I managed, by covering up with vast voluminous shirts (three sizes above my normal!) and a huge degree of desperate bravado to do the business. This makes it sound easy but it does take time, determination and a lot of effort: the more tired I got as the disrupted nights took their toll, the more difficult it became to induce the let-down reflex. I have now had to stop expressing during the daytime at work. Patricia

Find out what facilities your employers provide. You also need to find out if there are any potentially harmful toxins or chemicals at work that may affect breast-feeding. One particular concern, for example, is possible exposure to lead while breast-feeding, as this toxic metal can enter the breast milk and affect a breast-fed infant.

Bottle-feeding

A variety of studies have shown the beneficial effects of breast milk on a baby's emotional, physical and intellectual development. Not everyone is able or willing to breast-feed – especially if you need to return to work – in which case modern formula milks enriched with long-chain polyunsaturates (LCPs) are the next best thing. It is vitally important to sterilize all equipment (until your baby is at least six months old – ask your health visitor for advice) and to make up the formula to the exact strength intended. Formula made up too strong or too weak quickly leads to problems with weight gain (or lack of it) and fluid balance. Sterilizing bottles and having to warm milk to the right temperature can be quite a hassle, especially at night. In contrast, breast milk comes in its own container, at the right strength and temperature, and is instantly on tap when your baby needs it.

My baby went to a childminder near where I worked so I could visit for breast-feeds during my tea breaks and lunch-hour. Sharne

I drove home in the lunch hour to breast-feed. In between, I expressed milk and kept it chilled in the fridge at work ready for my baby to have next day while I was out of the house. Mary-Ann

I breast-fed my first baby and night feeds were so easy. I just rolled over, opened my special feeding nightie and carried on dozing while the baby took his fill. With the second baby I had to bottle feed after a month because my milk just dried up. Having to get out of bed to boil the kettle and mix the feed was a nuisance as it woke me up so I couldn't get back to sleep. The baby had to wait longer and used to get upset, too. Karen

The day I knew I was giving my second baby his last feed, I cried and cried. It seemed like our special bond was being taken away. Chris

I wish I could have breast-fed, given all its advantages, but I couldn't because I'd had plastic surgery years before to reduce the gross size of my breasts. All that sterilizing is rather a fiddle. On the other hand, bottle-feeding meant that my husband could share the process (and loved it), and avoided all those problems of engorgement, leaking milk, finding a convenient and discreet place. Cecilia

Weaning

Once it is time to wean your baby (usually some time between four and six months of age – your health visitor will advise) you will have to decide whether to give bottled or canned baby-food (many ranges, especially the organic ones, are delicious), or home prepared and puréed food. The majority of mothers use a combination of both.

Crying

Babies cry more than you think. Two hours a day tends to be the average during the first year and up to four hours crying is not unusual. By six weeks of age, one in four babies cry for three or more hours a day. Those with colic may cry for twice as long. Some babies cry very little however and if you meet all their needs for food, warmth, cuddles, interaction and comfort you may have a peaceful time. Having a baby constantly crying can be devastating on nerves, confidence and sanity – for help, contact Serene and the Cry-Sis helpline (see Resources, page 242).

We were driven to distraction when our baby kept crying all night with colic. Nothing helped until, in desperation, I got into the car in my dressing-gown and drove round the block with the baby until the movement lulled him to sleep. John

My friend's baby cried more than any other baby I know. We rallied round to give her a few hours' break but it was wearing for just one hour, let alone 24 hours a day. In the end, the doctor told them to leave the baby safely in his cot in the warm kitchen and go to bed themselves, just ignoring him. He wouldn't come to any harm and the parents desperately needed sleep. He would cry non-stop whether they were with him or not. He eventually grew out of it at around four months. Anne

A professional on ...
Weaning your baby

I had the luxury of working from home, which meant I could have the best of all worlds – being 100 percent on hand for my beautiful new son and still able to work. Among other benefits, this allowed me to keep my sanity while living in the world of nappies. But was I really going to prepare all his food from fresh, keep him away from all unhealthy but tempting goodies and in all respects feed him in the ideal manner? Of course not – theory and practice are not always at one. But I did decide to make a concerted effort to find a good source of organic vegetables, fruit, eggs and meat. I had started to do some research for a book offering practical advice to parents who wanted to get their children's diet right most of the time, if not all the time, and I became increasingly disturbed about the pollutants in our food chain and the impact these could have on the small, developing body of a child. I have wavered in the subsequent three years about many things, but this is a change that we have made permanent. In any event, I believe it is easier to get a toddler to eat up vegetables if they taste delicious, and organic ones do.

Small children are totally dependent upon their parents, and it is quite overwhelming when you think of the responsibility that this implies. And yet, despite this total dependence, they are still individual little people with their own identities. It can be the most startling moment when a new parent realizes that their little darling's wishes are not necessarily in accord with their own – especially in relation to food. So, no my little boy is not the perfect example of a controlled nutritional programme. Of course, he gets treats, and of course he blackmails me from time to time by refusing food or having a tantrum. But generally we have a good working relationship about food and I figure that if I let him have treats, but attempt to ensure they are wholesome treats, keep the additives to a minimum so as not to tax his little system, and do my best to provide healthy and tasty food at mealtimes – he's happy and I'm happy.

Suzannah Olivier, nutritionist and author of *What Should I Feed My Baby?* (Weidenfeld & Nicolson)

We were told babies sleep through the night within a few months of birth. Get real. Two years on, we haven't yet had an undisturbed night! Steve

My husband gave up smoking during the preconceptual care period to ensure his sperm were healthy. Unfortunately, he started again during my pregnancy due to the stress of exams. He never, ever smokes in the house or anywhere near the baby. He goes out to the garage or in the garden. We now want another baby so he is psyching himself up to stop smoking again. Belinda

Sleep

During the first few months, your baby will spend a lot of time asleep as they need around 14-16 hours sleep a day. Although it is commonly believed that babies should sleep through the night by the age of six months, few do. And even when they do sleep through the night, they commonly work on a different internal alarm clock from their parents' and wake up demanding attention at the crack of dawn.

Allergies

To help avoid allergies such as asthma, don't let anyone smoke cigarettes anywhere near your infant and preferably not in your house at all. Some experts also advise washing family dogs and cats weekly to reduce housedust mites which thrive in shed animal fur. This also reduces animal danders (shed fur/skin) that can cause allergies in their own right. This may be worth considering if there is a tendency towards allergies on either side of the new baby's family.

Contraception

Research shows that women who are not breast-feeding may ovulate as early as 28 days after delivery. The first six to nine months after delivery are peak times for accidental pregnancy, so decide well in advance on what type of contraception you want to use after your baby is born. You may wish to change from the method you used before having your baby, especially if you are hoping to conceive again within a year or so. This is something to talk over with your doctor or practice nurse.

A doctor came round in the hospital to ask what I was going to use for contraception. At that point, I felt I never wanted to see another penis again, let alone make nookey with one. As I was breast-feeding, I didn't fancy taking the mini-Pill as the hormones do get into the milk. Condoms seemed the best option – not that I expected to use them for some time. Jilly

Hair loss after pregnancy

During pregnancy, many women find their hair becomes thicker and glossier. After pregnancy however, there may be significant hair loss that can cause temporary thinning.

Around four to six weeks after having your baby, you may notice a sudden increase in the amount of hair you lose. This effect is known as telogen effluvium. Not every woman experiences it for the effects range from hardly noticeable to 50 percent hair loss. Thinning will slowly improve as resting hair follicles reactivate at different rates and hair life cycles lose their synchronicity. In some cases, telogen effluvium is linked with nutrient deficiencies, especially of protein or iron. You can help to reduce telogen effluvium by taking a vitamin and mineral supplement designed for pregnancy while expecting your baby, and by continuing to take a good vitamin and mineral supplement afterwards, too.

Sex after pregnancy

A 1994 Gallup survey on behalf of First Response found that 42 percent of women questioned who had had, or intended to have a baby, would say 'No!' to sex for at least six to eight weeks after the birth, with one in a hundred saying 'No!' for over a year.

While sex is likely to be off the agenda for a while as a result of discomfort, stitches, hormone changes and the blood-stained discharge that lasts for at least six weeks after childbirth, it is important to show love in other ways during these early weeks.

> No one warned me that I would have a blood-stained discharge for at least six weeks after delivery. While I loved the smell of it – like buttermilk – it embarrassed me enough to hold my husband at arms' length. It eventually disappeared after eight weeks, although my sex drive didn't reappear for at least four months after delivery. My midwife said this was a normal, hormonal side-effect of breast-feeding. Jo

> I found sex painful for months after giving birth – mostly due to the stitches I had, but also as one of the effects of breast-feeding. My partner was understanding but was starting to get irritable from what he described as a build-up of testosterone. I started taking Agnus castus extracts which both boost milk production and increase sex drive. I started to feel sexy again quite quickly. Emma

> I was surprised at how sexual I felt within a few days of childbirth. Producing a child made me aware that sexuality is part of the reproductive system. When I made love after I gave birth to my son, I had to have a towel wrapped around my breasts to soak up the copious supply of milk which was pouring out. Jude

During pregnancy, my hair was gloriously thick and glossy – along with my nails which I was able to grow for the first time in my life. Four weeks after having the baby, I suddenly started moulting. Clumps of hair stuck in my brush, and blocked the sink when washing my hair. I panicked. Luckily, I found Lucinda at Attention X [see Resources, page 238] who helped me cope, and inserted fibres using medical hair design techniques that hid my bald patches until they regrew. Linda

Pelvic floor exercises

Pelvic floor exercises should form part of every woman's health regime long before wanting to have a baby, throughout pregnancy and through into old age. They only take a few minutes, and can be done just about anywhere. Start now!

Following childbirth, the vaginal muscles will be stretched. Pelvic floor exercises will tone and strengthen these muscles and help to prevent or reduce the urinary leakage that can occur towards the end of pregnancy and during the first few months after childbirth. Around one in four women find they leak urine when they cough, sneeze or run after having recently had a baby. This usually improves although around one in ten women continue to have some degree of problem. Here are some of the most commonly recommended exercises:

- Pull up the front and back passages tightly as if trying to stop the bowels from opening. Hold tight for a count of four and repeat this every quarter of an hour.

- When going to the loo, practice stopping the flow of urine mid-stream. Initially this will be difficult but when it becomes easy, do this at least once a day. When you've learned to identify which muscles are squeezed during this action, you can then practise clenching them several times a day even when not urinating.

- Stand with your feet apart and your knees slightly bent. Place your hands on your hips, jut your bottom out and rotate your pelvis slowly in a clockwise direction. Continue rotating your pelvis round to form a complete circle that is as wide as possible. Continue these pelvic gyrations for one to two minutes, then gyrate your pelvis round in an anti-clockwise direction for another one to two minutes.

- Stand with your feet wide apart, and squat right down so your knees are bent and your bottom is just off the floor. Rest your fingers or palms on the floor between your feet, and let your buttocks drop down as far as possible. Breathe in deeply, then out, letting your anus and pelvic floor muscles relax. Then breathe in four or five short breaths without exhaling in between. With each breath in, draw up and tighten your pelvic floor muscles as if pulling up your vagina step by step. Then breathe out five times slowly (without inhaling in between) and release your pelvic floor muscles in short steps. Repeat ten times.

- Pull in the pelvic floor muscles before coughing, sneezing or lifting and avoid standing for long periods of time.
- Generally increase your level of exercise – research shows that pelvic floor muscles can also be strengthened beneficially by swimming, yoga, walking and other keep fit activities.

For women with a pronounced or continuing problem, weighted cones to tighten and tone vaginal muscles – and make pelvic floor exercises more efficient – are also available. These vaginal cones (Aquaflex) are inserted like a tampon for up to ten minutes twice a day and are available from large branches of Boots the Chemist, or by mail order (see also Resources, page 235).

Postnatal depression

After you have given birth, it is common to suffer so-called baby blues. Feelings of low mood, unhappiness, tearfulness, irritability, anxiety and extreme tiredness occur four to five days after giving birth in 50-80 percent of new mothers. Symptoms usually improve within a week or two and are due to the rapid adjustments in hormone levels occurring at this time. Around one in ten new mothers suffer from a more severe postnatal depression however whose symptoms include:

- despondency
- lack of interest in the baby or themselves
- feelings of not being able to cope
- feelings of guilt, inadequacy and rejection
- irritability
- anxiety and panic attacks
- difficulty in sleeping
- difficulty in concentrating
- loss of appetite
- loss of interest in sex
- difficulty bonding with, or feeling love for, the new baby.

Always tell your doctor, health visitor or midwife if you start to feel depressed after childbirth. It is important to be aware in advance that this can occur, so that if symptoms develop you seek help early

I developed postnatal depression after my first baby. I was crying all the time and also felt guilty because I knew this was supposed to be the happiest time of my life – we had looked forward to the baby so much. My midwife, health visitor and family were brilliant. It took two months for the antidepressants to work. I tried hard to bond with my baby but it took weeks before I felt like a normal new mum again. It put me off having a second child, but I did and this time everything went OK, and apart from mild baby blues, I was fine. Sal

My wife developed postnatal psychosis and seemed to hate the baby at first. She was hearing voices and used to talk about hurting herself and the child. It was terrifying. They were admitted to the Mother and Baby unit of the local psychiatric hospital for their own safety. She is now back to normal, but I didn't trust her on her own with our son for over a year. It has put us off trying for another child and we have decided to stick with just the one.
Trevor

during the condition rather than later. If you have postnatal depression it must be diagnosed and treated as early as possible. Treatment involves close emotional support. Antidepressant drugs or hormone treatment may also be needed. It is also helpful if family members are aware of the symptoms to look for as the mother herself may not at first realize that anything is wrong, or she may be reluctant to seek help. For more information, contact the Association for Post-Natal Illness (see Resources, page 235).

A professional on ...
Postnatal depression

Postnatal depression is common but often starts insidiously and, tragically, is often unrecognized. It can completely spoil a mother's enjoyment of her newborn baby. And, since effective treatment is available, the sooner it is sorted out the better, for both mother and child. Research has shown that babies who have happy mothers develop better than babies whose mothers are depressed seriously enough for it to be a medical problem. (I'm not talking about just the well-known baby blues that make many women a bit tearful and unhappy for a few days after childbirth.)

If, when you've had a good try, and you seriously feel that you are not coping, have lost your self-esteem, or if everything seems grey in this new phase of your life, postnatal depression may be at the root of your problem. It can happen to anyone, so don't be afraid to seek the advice of your GP or your health visitor if you feel it might be happening to you. They may well have experienced it themselves.

Well-known author and agony aunt Claire Rayner, and actress Sinead Cussack, are among the many successful women who knew the misery that it can cause, and who overcame it, with sympathetic professional help. So don't suffer in silence if you ever have a feeling that life with your baby is running out of control and you are too exausted to cope. But hopefully, you will have got help before this ever happens.

Dr Ann Whitehead, GP

A professional on ...
The Pill and postnatal illness

Many mothers start to take the Pill as soon as their doctor will let them after birth. If a mother is at all depressed, she should stop taking the Pill at the earliest opportunity, even if she is loath to do so. The Pill can cause depression in some women and it is seen as an aggravating factor where a woman is depressed after birth. It is however very important that the depressed mother does not become pregnant, because she will probably need drug treatment which cannot be given in early pregnancy. Also a further birth can sometimes make the mother more depressed and in this state she has two very young babies to cope with.

For a woman who is suffering from depression, several methods of birth control can be used. Both the sheath and the cap when used properly give adequate protection against pregnancy and are easy to use.

The Association for Postnatal Illness

Chapter 13:
Special Cases

Thinking about starting a family is a time of great joy and hope. It can also be the start of a lifetime of extended problems. When preparing to take the leap from single person to parent, most people assume there will be a happy outcome with the birth of a perfectly healthy, and usually singleton, baby. Having a single, healthy baby will transform your life. Conceiving a multiple pregnancy, or a child with special needs, will have an immeasurably greater impact.

While many readers may wish to skip this chapter, it is worth giving a passing thought to how you would cope with:

- premature menopause
- miscarriage
- deciding whether to terminate your pregnancy because of a foetal abnormality
- having a very premature or low birth weight baby
- conceiving twins or more
- wanting a baby if you are found to be HIV positive
- adopting a baby if you were unable to have a child the traditional way.

Premature menopause

Premature menopause can run in families. It may be due to inheriting fewer egg follicles than normal, eggs with a shorter life span or to an overactive immune system that interferes with the way the ovaries work. It has also been suggested that women whose periods start at an early age may find that they stop later than normal. There is little scientific evidence to prove these common beliefs, however. Several other factors are known to be linked with premature menopause:

- Research suggests that heavy smokers will reach the menopause 18-24 months earlier than non-smokers. This is because several chemicals (e.g. nicotine, arabinase, conitine) in cigarette smoke affect oestrogen metabolism so that lower levels occur.

- Excess alcohol can lower oestrogen levels, shrink the ovaries, damage egg follicles and trigger a premature menopause; the level of alcohol that could cause this varies from woman to woman, depending on how their metabolism handles alcohol and how much exercise they take. Government guidelines suggest that women should drink no more than two or three units of alcohol per day. Weekly intakes of over 35 units are considered dangerous for women.

- High levels of stress can affect hormone balance and is a well-known cause of a period being late or missed altogether. In the same way, excessive stress such as illness, severe financial problems or bereavement may trigger an early menopause although this is uncommon and poorly understood.

- Infection with the mumps virus can cause inflammation of the ovaries and damage large numbers of egg follicles. This is rare, but has been known to result in an early menopause.

- Some types of drug treatment may temporarily or permanently affect the ovaries to produce symptoms of an early menopause. Drugs which can produce a temporary, reversible menopause include danazol, buserelin, goserelin, leuprorelin and nafarelin which are most commonly prescribed to treat endometriosis. Periods usually return to normal between three and eight weeks of stopping treatment, and false menopause symptoms disappear.

- Radiotherapy and chemotherapy for cancer may produce a permanent early menopause. Younger women have a better chance of their ovaries recovering after cancer treatment than older women, although if many egg follicles have been damaged or destroyed by the treatment, those that remain may not last very long. It is now also possible for a section of ovarian tissue, complete with egg follicles, to be removed and frozen before treatment starts, providing an opportunity for fertility treatment to take place using the woman's own eggs in the future. The technology to allow this routinely has not yet been fully developed.

Some women experiencing a premature menopause have not run

out of eggs, but those that are present have stopped responding to the normal hormone cycle. This is known as resistant ovary syndrome. In some cases the ovaries may recover spontaneously but this should not be relied on. The only way to diagnose this properly is through a biopsy to see if living egg follicles are present in ovarian tissue.

The symptoms of an early menopause are similar to those that would have occurred in later life but may be more severe if oestrogen levels fall rapidly. Periods may become irregular and lighter or heavier than usual. The early symptoms of the menopause include:

- hot flushes and night sweats
- difficulty sleeping
- anxiety
- irritability
- mood swings
- tiredness
- headaches
- pins and needles
- poor concentration
- loss of self-esteem
- feelings of distance from those around you.

Using the oral contraceptive Pill will mask the symptoms of an early menopause as a withdrawal bleed will still occur each month. You will not realize you have been through the menopause until you stop taking the Pill and your periods fail to return.

Taking the Pill does not cause an early menopause however – it may even protect against it by helping to conserve your eggs.

Premature menopause may be diagnosed by blood tests that measure circulating levels of follicle-stimulating hormone (FSH), leutinizing hormone (LH) and oestradiol. Premature menopause is suggested if FSH and LH levels are raised above a certain level and oestradiol levels are correspondingly low.

Women who suffer from a premature menopause may still be able to get pregnant naturally although their fertility will be low. If you have not already fulfilled your wish to become a mother, or to have as many children as you would wish, and still want to have a baby, assisted fertility techniques may help. Fertility drugs may be tried to stimulate release of any remaining eggs. Receiving donor eggs or embryos is also a possibility although national waiting lists

I started taking the Pill after my second child was born and took it for eight years. We then thought about having another child – I was lonely at home all day on my own – but when I stopped the Pill, at the age of 36, nothing happened. I've never had another period since. Tina

I didn't think I wanted children, but when I was 37 it was as if my body knew my biological clock was ticking. I developed these amazing longings to have a baby. I didn't realize maternal urges could be so strong. Sara

We didn't exactly decide when to have a baby. We'd embarked on marriage with the expectation of having a family, waited a couple of years before 'trying', had one unsuccessful pregnancy (death in utero), and carried on trying until it happened. I was a very elderly primigravida, having married late (29) and actually achieved No.1 daughter at 36. Cecilia

are high – there is an acute shortage of egg donors and volunteers are desperately needed. Adoption is another possibility.

> I was devastated to experience a premature menopause at the age of 30. I had had menopausal symptoms for three years, but assumed they were related to the endometriosis I developed in my early twenties. After trying to conceive unsuccessfully, I underwent two courses of fertility treatment. On the first attempt eight follicles were drained, but they only found one shell and no eggs. I decided to try again and to my horror I only produced two small follicles which meant the cycle had to be aborted. I couldn't believe this was happening to us. I then had a hormone profile that showed my remaining ovary had stopped functioning. I cried floods of tears and was so upset I had to take eight weeks off work. I am now hoping to become pregnant using donor eggs, but unfortunately there is a national shortage.[5] Suzann

Although the menopause marks the final few tick-tocks on a woman's reproductive clock, fertility does decline with increasing age before the menopause is reached which increases the pressure to start trying for a baby sooner rather than later. Having said that, if her family is complete, any woman whose last period occurred before the age of 50 should still use an effective method of contraception for two years. (For more information, see chapter 9.) An excellent book that explores why more and more women are delaying having children, and the joys and challenges of late motherhood, is *Beating the Biological Clock* by Pamela Armstrong (Headline).

Miscarriage

A miscarriage is the early failure of pregnancy before the 24th week of gestation. After this time, the sad occurrence of a foetal death is known as a stillbirth. Most women are surprised to learn that as many as one in three newly fertilized eggs fail to implant in the wall of the uterus. Of those that do successfully implant and start to produce a placenta, it is estimated that at least another one in three miscarry – often before the mother is even aware she is pregnant. The reasons for this are unknown, but are likely to result from one-off chromosome abnormalities of the egg or sperm, toxins (e.g. from smoking, drugs, excess alcohol), nutrient deficiencies, infection, hormone imbalances (e.g. not enough placental hormones

---

[5] If anyone would consider donating eggs, please phone St Thomas' Hospital on 0171-633 0152 quoting ref. number R1446. A screening questionnaire will be sent and counselling given to women before they decide whether or not to go ahead.

to stop the next period from starting) or pre-existing maternal conditions such as high blood pressure, anaemia, diabetes, thyroid problems or certain immune diseases. Sadly, of all pregnancies that are advanced enough to be recognized by the mother, around one in seven (15 percent) will fail to progress beyond the first 20 weeks. Twice as many will threaten to miscarry, with spotting of blood and/or period-like abdominal pains.

After a woman has had one miscarriage, her risk of another is twice that of a woman who has not previously had one. After two consecutive miscarriages, the risk increases so that around 30 percent of future pregnancies miscarry. The risks do not increase greatly with each subsequent miscarriage, however. A couple experiencing recurrent miscarriages therefore have a good chance of an eventual, happy outcome. A couple who have had two consecutive miscarriages has a 70 percent chance of successfully becoming parents, while for those who have had six or more miscarriages, the chance of becoming parents is still 50 percent.

A couple who have experienced one or more miscarriages are usually advised to follow a preconceptual care programme. The charity Foresight can also offer ongoing support, nutritional information and advice. Although it may not seem like it, having a miscarriage does offer hope – it shows that both partners are fertile, and are therefore one step further down the road to becoming parents than those experiencing infertility.

We were devastated to experience three miscarriages one after the other. It felt like we would never successfully have a family. The doctors could find nothing wrong, which in many ways made it all worse. It felt like a personal failure on my part. We contacted the charity, Foresight, and they were brilliant. We followed their suggestions and advice and now have two healthy children. I can't thank them enough.
Gemma

My third pregnancy was different. I was very ill for the first 16 weeks, then it stopped like someone switching off a light. Then I bled. At first I wouldn't believe what was happening but in the end knew I had to do something. I had a scan, the registrar showed me what he could see, my beautiful perfect little baby and another empty sac with just a little blob in it. He said he was very sorry. I couldn't work for the rest of the pregnancy as I was supposed to rest; difficult with two other children. I went through the rest of the pregnancy carrying one dead baby and one alive, with the constant risk of losing the other. I switched off. I didn't plan at all for the birth. Later I wondered if I would have felt the same if I hadn't seen the scan.

When my son was born, the other sac and twin had been squashed beyond recognition. The midwife's query as to whether I had had any problems during my pregnancy seemed so insensitive and it felt

I was shocked to discover my baby was abnormal. I was then faced with the harsh decision about whether or not to terminate the pregnancy. In many ways, I was lucky as my baby had heart failure, haemolytic anaemia and severe fluid retention – a condition known as hydrops fetalis. This meant there was little chance of my baby surviving even if I went to full term. The decision about whether or not to terminate would have been so much more difficult if the child had the possibility of a good quality of life as, for example, in Down's syndrome. Kate

as though she was rubbing salt into the wound. I then experienced the worst pain imaginable. The pain of loss and grief, of being incomplete ... I would have given my life for just a second to touch that baby, or smell it, or see it. The pain wasn't just emotional, it was physical pain. I thought at the time I had found my soul, because it felt like someone had torn my soul from my body. I felt I could no longer feel happiness, I couldn't laugh; just cry and cry and cry ... Jane

Miscarriage can be heartbreaking for prospective fathers as well, yet many men whose partners have suffered a miscarriage feel unable to openly express their grief. They may experience strong feelings of sorrow and loss for their unborn child, but as they are encouraged to take on a supportive role for their partner, their own feelings are often ignored. This apparent lack of grief can be interpreted as lack of caring, making the man's sense of loss and exclusion even greater. It is vital that men are given space to grieve after miscarriage, too. Couples should ask their GP for a joint referral for counselling. The National Childbirth Trust and the Miscarriage Association (see Resources pages 236 and 240) are also able to provide information and support for couples experiencing the grief of miscarriage.

Termination for abnormality

Another horror that some expectant couples have to face is the knowledge that their baby is abnormal, necessitating a decision about whether or not to terminate the pregnancy. Sadly, between 2 and 5 percent of babies conceived have a major congenital malformation which will be associated with a variety of special needs.

When faced with such a difficult decision, it is essential to know that the national charity, Support Around Termination For Abnormality (SATFA) is available to befriend and support those couples who are considering having antenatal testing, who are waiting anxiously for test results, and who are faced with the difficult decision about whether or not to end an abnormal pregnancy.

Pre-term and low birth weight babies

Pre-term babies

The normal length of pregnancy is 38 to 42 weeks. Any baby born

A professional on ...
Coping with miscarriage

When my husband and I decided to have a large family of four children, we assumed it would just happen, because that was what we wanted. Unfortunately, I suffered four miscarriages instead and was absolutely devastated. When we finally had a son, we were told to make the most of him as it was unlikely we would have any more. Now, at the age of 41, and having been married for 17 years, we finally have four healthy children. With the benefit of hindsight, I offer the following advice to anyone experiencing a miscarriage:

- At whatever stage you lose a baby, grieve first and make sure you are fully recovered before trying for another baby.

- Bear in mind that future pregnancies will never be anxiety-free, so plan how you will cope with putting your past experiences into perspective.

- Don't go for a baby at all costs. You need to set limits to what you are prepared to do. Despite your deep sadness about not having a baby, you must not damage the relationship you have with your partner – by making him feel like a sperm bank, for example. Cherish your relationship, partner, friends, family and the here and now. Don't risk damaging what you have got for the chance of something you may never get.

- Don't put your life on hold. No experience in life is wasted. Accept it and learn to let go. Do things you know you couldn't do if you had a child. If you've always wanted to go backpacking in Nepal, do it now. Take advantage of the positive side of not being a parent, for if you do eventually become one everything will change.

- In this 'let's talk about everything' society choose your confidantes very carefully. You are not obliged to explain to anyone why you do not have children (yet). It is easy to become pigeonholed by everyone as 'Jane who is trying for a baby but keeps having miscarriages', or 'Jane whose husband seems to be infertile'. While it can be positive to share your feelings in a support group or with your doctors, don't feel you have to explain your situation to everyone if you don't want to.

- Don't be too surprised if you suffer from depression after you successfully give birth to a baby. It is quite normal to have the baby blues — especially after the stress of worrying throughout your pregnancy about whether everything will turn out all right. And don't feel guilty if you do feel down. Never be afraid to tell your GP, health visitor or midwife if you feel depressed. It is nothing to be ashamed of. Fathers can suffer from this post high-adrenaline slump, too.

- If you are unable to have children, don't waste time beating yourself up over it. Lots of things happen in life for which we will never understand the reasons. There are lots of other ways in which you can experience the joy of interacting with children. Consider adoption, fostering, sponsorship or being a good godparent, aunt or uncle.

- Don't underestimate the power of prayer. I prayed to have all my children and strongly believe they are all a gift from God.

Charlotte, a member of the Miscarriage Association who suffered four miscarriages herself before 37 weeks of pregnancy is classed as premature or pre-term. A low birth weight baby is one weighing under 2,500g (5.5lbs) at delivery. Very low birth weight children weigh under 1,500g (3.3lbs) at birth, and extremely low birth weight weigh under 1,000g (2.2lbs). Most babies who are pre-term also have a low birth weight. Some babies born at the normal time (term) also have a low birth weight, due to factors such as poor maternal nutrition or the effects of alcohol, smoking or drugs.

As many as one in eight deliveries result in a pre-term, low birth weight baby. This is one of the biggest health risks a newborn faces. More babies die from being premature than from any other cause, although having said that, increasing numbers of babies born as early as 24 weeks are surviving thanks to advances in medical care.

> Our baby was born at 28 weeks and we were told her chance of survival was small. I went home, looked at our newly-painted nursery and just howled. After pulling myself together, I was determined to fight for my little girl and help her struggle for life. I spent just about all my waking hours in the Special Care Baby Unit, talking to her, stroking her and helping to feed her my expressed milk. She seemed to sense the love surrounding her and slowly improved. Now, at the age of two, she is a perfectly normal and delightful little girl. Chris

In up to half of all cases, the cause of spontaneous pre-term delivery is unknown. The main causes that have been identified include:

- multiple pregnancies (twins or more, especially when the babies are identical and share the same placenta)
- smoking cigarettes (including passive smoking)
- excessive alcohol intake
- illicit drug use
- uterine abnormalities (e.g. weak cervix, fibroids, abnormal shape)
- urinary or reproductive tract infections
- maternal asthma, especially poorly controlled asthma

Many of these risk factors are preventable. For more information on how to reduce the risk of pre-term birth, contact Tommy's Campaign (see Resources, page 236).

Our baby was born at 30 weeks. We were told that anything over 25 weeks improved her chances of survival. Nothing prepared us for the Special Care Baby Unit however, and seeing our scrap of a baby trailing tubes and leads from just about every available orifice and vein. She looked so helpless. The worst thing was not being able to cuddle her – just having to sit helplessly, stroking her hand, while she fought for life. We thought we were going to lose her. The day she eventually came home was by far the best day of my life. Jane

When I was told we were expecting triplets it seemed like an exciting way to get our family over with in one go. The birth was easy, but coping with three babies all hungry and crying at the same time was an absolute nightmare. Debra

I am HIV positive and want to have children, but am afraid the infection will be passed on. I couldn't bare the guilt of knowing I had given my child a death sentence like the one hanging over me. Allie

Low birth weight babies

Babies born at optimum birth weights (3.5-4.5kg/7.7-9.9lbs) have the lowest risk of developmental disorders such as those of the central nervous system. Unfortunately, those born with low birth weight, however, have a higher risk of physical or mental developmental problems, and are more likely to suffer from:

- cerebral palsy
- mental retardation
- faulty development of the lungs
- blindness
- deafness
- epilepsy.

Research shows a link between the size of a baby at birth and maternal diet at or around the time of conception – another reason why a preconceptual programme is so important (see chapter 8). Recent research also suggests that low birth weight babies are more likely to develop high blood pressure, coronary heart disease, stroke and insulin-dependent diabetes in later life. In fact, low birth weight quadruples the risk of heart disease in later life compared with the risk for larger babies.

Multiple pregnancy

When thinking about having a baby, most couples think in terms of one. Multiple births are becoming more common however, partly due to assisted conception techniques. At least one in 80 pregnancies results in twins or more. (Spare a thought for the parents of the world's first healthy septuplets, born in Iowa in November 1997 – they had to cope with 294 feeds and 245 nappy changes each week, involving a rota of 60 helpers weekly!)

A professional on ...
Multiple births

Couples undergoing treatment for fertility problems should be told of the risk of multiple pregnancy. The HFEA (Human Fertilization and Embryology Authority) even makes it obligatory for every centre performing IVF (in vitro fertilization) to offer counselling, so that would-be parents do know they could have twins, triplets or more. However, there is a big difference between hearing what is said and absorbing all the practical implications.

A couple may be so desperate for a child that multiple pregnancy seems a small price to pay and they are likely to underestimate the risks as well as the problems. Older women especially may feel that time is running out. Others may even welcome the thought of an instant family, particularly if they are making huge sacrifices to fund their treatment, as many do when unable to obtain it on the NHS. Twins and higher multiples bring many challenges, starting with a pregnancy that is more demanding physically and emotionally, and more likely to be complicated by both minor symptoms like morning sickness, and major complications like pre-eclampsia and premature labour. Multiple births also have a higher rate of medical intervention, with 25 percent of twins being born by Caesarean. On arrival, multiples are more likely to be small and more vulnerable than singletons. Once home, the new mother is likely to be exhausted by trying to satisfy the needs of more than one baby at once. A mother of triplets once estimated that baby care and related household chores ate up 197.5 hours per week. Since there are only 168 hours in a week, extra help has to be enlisted (and funded). Unfortunately state-funded help is non-existent for twins and scanty even for triplets and quads. As some mothers have found, it is useless being offered three hours help a week when one does not know in advance when those hours might be, or even on which day of the week.

Dr Carol Cooper, from her book, *Twins and Multiple Births – the essential parenting guide from pregnancy to adulthood* (Vermilion)

A professional on ...

Wanting to have a baby when you are HIV positive

The Terrence Higgins Trust provides support and information for women who are thinking of having a baby and are HIV positive, or think they may have been exposed to some risk of HIV infection. The following facts may be of interest.

- *Risks of infection to the mother comes from:*
  - having unprotected sexual intercourse with an infected person
  - receiving an infected blood transfusion
  - sharing needles and syringes when injecting drugs.

- *If the pregnant woman is HIV positive:* the virus can be passed on from mother to baby during pregnancy, and childbirth. This is known as vertical transmission. In the UK, 85 percent of all paediatric AIDS cases are passed on from mother to child. Breast-feeding doubles the risk of transmission.

- *HIV antibody tests* are blood tests which look for the presence of HIV antibodies to show whether the person has been exposed to HIV and is infected with the virus.

'CD4 counts' measure the number of CD4 cells in a cubic millilitre of blood, indicating the efficiency of the immune system and the state of health of the individual. A level of between 200 and 500 shows that some damage has been done, leaving the individual with reduced immunity.

'Viral load' tests estimate the number of HIV particles in a sample of blood. A high viral load indicates that the immune system is at risk of being damaged by the high levels of virus present in the blood and that the individual is highly infectious.

Timing the pregnancy to correspond with a time when the CD4 count is high and the viral load is low has been shown to reduce the chances of exposing the baby to the virus. Taking zidovudine (AZT) has also been shown to reduce the chance of exposure by two thirds.

- *What are the risks of unsafe sex with an infected or non-infected partner to the woman and her baby?* For a person who is HIV positive – even if they are receiving treatment – unsafe sex carries the risk of possible infection with sexually transmitted diseases like herpes. This can increase the viral load (see above), no matter what the partner's HIV status. There is also the risk of reinfection with another, drug-resistant form of HIV. Combination treatments attack the virus and suppress its reproduction, therefore helping the immune system to recover, but it may not be able to do this with a drug-resistant strain.

- *What are the long-term effects of HIV treatment taken during pregnancy to the mother/baby?* The use of zidovudine (AZT) in pregnancy, during delivery and for the baby after it is born is known to reduce the risk of transmission of HIV from the mother to the baby. The long-term effects of combination therapies are still unknown. Some women start treatment after 14 weeks of pregnancy to reduce risk of congenital defects on the baby. There are no reported long-term effects from taking zidovudine on the baby except for a mild form of anaemia, which was resolved once treatment was stopped.

  By receiving treatment, the woman has the benefit of boosting her immune system. She should also take positive action to stay well by eating a healthy diet, resting and avoiding stress, as well as taking the opportunity to link in with HIV services and find out more about HIV and support networks.

- *Delivery:* Caesarean birth reduces the chance of the baby being infected as there is reduced direct contact between maternal and foetal blood, but if birth is by Caesarean section, delivery must take place in hospital. The advantage of this is that both mother and baby can be monitored closely and any emergencies dealt with immediately. The disadvantage is that the mother's HIV status may become known to more health professionals, and this is worrying for some women.

- *Breast-feeding:* HIV contained in breast milk may be passed on by breast-feeding, so women who are HIV positive are advised not to breast-feed their baby.

Liz Kawonza, the Terrence Higgins Trust

We are unable to have children as my tubes are blocked and my husband's sperm count is low. We thought long and hard about all the alternatives but eventually decided not to adopt. Having children is a major sacrifice. I would be happy to make sacrifices for my own flesh and blood, but am worried that I may resent a child who isn't biologically mine if he or she stops me doing the things I want to do. Jo

We adopted a little boy four years ago and have just heard we can now adopt a two-year-old girl. I am so excited I can hardly breathe. We love our little boy so much – he has brought so much joy and laughter into our lives. The fact that I am not his birth mother seems totally irrelevant. Rachel

Being HIV positive

The Human Deficiency Virus (HIV) is now very much part of our society. Carrying the virus has important implications for your desire to become a parent. These problems are not insurmountable however.

HIV and sperm

For men who are HIV positive, there is the worry of passing on HIV infection to their partner and their future child. While you can practise safe sex at other times, using a condom is not compatible with wanting to conceive a child. Assisted conception techniques are available that allow HIV positive men to father healthy children without increasing the risk of infecting an HIV negative partner. This involves collecting a semen sample and 'washing' it to remove the infective fraction. The most motile sperm are then isolated and used to artificially inseminate the partner after inducing ovulation. It is estimated that the technique has only a 4 percent risk of inseminating the mother with infected sperm such that she subsequently becomes HIV positive. In a trial involving 29 couples, 59 insemination attempts resulted in 17 pregnancies in 15 women. Each woman required between one and five insemination attempts each. None of the women became HIV positive and all babies were HIV negative at follow-ups ranging from six months to three years.

Adoption

For most people who are unable to conceive their own children adoption is an obvious answer to their desire to have a baby, but it is by no means an easy option, especially if you are hoping to care for a tiny infant. Most of the issues surrounding adoption are covered in the following two contributions from Parent-to-Parent Information on Adoption Services (PPIAS) and the British Agencies for Adoption & Fostering.

A professional on ...
Adoption

'**I** want to become a parent' is probably more appropriate to adoption today than 'I want to have a baby'. There are very few babies needing adoption now, due to factors such as improved contraception, easier access to abortion and a more relaxed attitude towards single parenthood. Adoption is a service for children who need new families, not a service for childless couples, although the needs of both may be mutually fulfilled through adoption. The children who need adoption nowadays are likely to be older (aged from two years up to early teens), physically disabled, have learning difficulties, be part of a sibling group, or to need parents from a specific ethnic background.

Adoption is a valid way of building a family but it is not the 'easy way'. Parenting someone else's child is not the same as having your own, although it can be just as rewarding. There are subtle differences between birth and adoption which are not always evident or easily explainable, and can often only be really understood by other adoptive families.

There are particular qualities which help people to be 'good enough' parents to adopted children. Love is an important factor, but on its own is not enough. Children who need a new family will have suffered some trauma in their lives: they may have been abused or neglected; they will probably have had a number of different homes and different people looking after them; they may have formed attachments to people and been parted from them, or they may have formed no attachments at all. Adoptive parents need to be strong and wise and loving with a good sense of humour. They must not expect instant bonding and must have an understanding of how abuse and neglect in the early years of a child's life can continue to affect them as they grow up.

If you adopt, you will love your adopted children just as much as if you had borne them, but you won't have the same clues as to how they will develop, who they will look like, what talents and skills will blossom in them. You will probably work harder at building a relationship, and be an extremely conscientious parent. At the same time, you may have to face prejudice and stand up for your conviction that you are just as much a 'real' parent as someone whose child was born to them. You will have to help your children understand why they had to be adopted, and give them as positive an image of their background as possible. This is not always easy, especially when the background was one of abuse or neglect.

As adopted children grow up, they will understand adoption in different ways and as adults may be better able to comprehend the pressures and difficulties their birth parents suffered. It is increasingly common in adoption nowadays for children to retain some contact with birth families. This can range from the exchange of information, letters, and birthday cards, either directly or through a third party (usually the agency which placed the child), to phone calls or face-to-face meetings. Contact can be with birth parents, siblings, grandparents or other members of the family. Any contact arrangements made should always be in the best interests of the child, and should be flexible enough to allow for changes in frequency, length or nature as the child's needs change.

Adoptive parents are sometimes reluctant to seek help if there are difficulties within the family, as they are afraid to be seen as 'failing' as parents. But adoptive parenting is different from biological parenting, and if you encounter difficulties these may arise from things that happened in the child's life before you knew them. Joining an adoptive parent group such as PPIAS can be a very effective source of support and advice (even from as early as when you first start thinking about adoption). You should also approach the agency you adopted through, your local social services department or one of the specialized post-adoption services for further support if problems occur, even years after the adoption. Never struggle alone with problems.

The great majority of adoptions work perfectly well and are a source of great joy and satisfaction to both parents and children. If adoption is the route you choose to parenthood, then enjoy the journey!

Patricia Swanton, Editor of *Adoption UK, the Quarterly Journal of PPIAS*

A professional on ...
The need for more adopters

'Getting adopted is like sitting down after standing up for a long time.' (quote from
a ten-year-old adopted child)

Adopting a child will arguably be the most momentous commitment you make
during your lifetime. You will become a parent to, and provide a home for, a child
who needs it. There are currently up to 10,000 children in care who are waiting for a
permanent family. The majority are living with foster carers who undoubtedly give
them love and support. Nevertheless they are not the family for life that these
children need.

At the British Agencies for Adoption & Fostering (BAAF) we are frequently asked
by the media and public if we think it should be 'easier' to adopt. The insinuation in
the question is that it is currently too hard. Well, yes the current assessment process
is intensive, rigorous and demanding – 'hard', if you wish. But choosing a family for a
child is an enormous decision to make on their behalf. It's never going to be easy and
it never should.

In 1995 (the last year for which we have figures) almost 6,000 children were
adopted. We estimate that over half of this number were step-parent adoptions and
fewer than 3,000 children were adopted into new homes. Research that BAAF has
done on these figures shows the average age of a child being adopted was five years,
eight months old. Only 322 infants under 12 months old were adopted.

This is the pattern of adoption today. Very few babies are relinquished at birth and
the majority of children adopted have spent time in foster care. Many will have had
difficult and sad childhoods; they may have been removed from their birth families
because of parental neglect or abuse. As they try to make sense of their feelings of
rejection, anger and pain some children will exhibit challenging and demanding
behaviour. Should it ever be 'easy' to adopt these children? Of course not.

There are many myths about the assessment process and adoption criteria that we need to debunk. It may surprise you to know, for example, that there is no upper age limit for adoption (our research has revealed 50-year-olds and over who adopt), no criteria on marital status (single adopters currently make up approximately 8 percent of all adopters), and there are no requirements regarding income (as long as you can demonstrate financial security). The only thing that will prohibit an applicant from adopting will be a previous offence or conviction against a child. Otherwise all applicants will be assessed in terms of what they can offer the child.

Adoption has changed enormously since the 'peak years' of the late 1960s and early 1970s. There has been a massive shift in ethos among those working with children and their families. Adoption is now much more about finding families for children, as opposed to finding children for families. That's not just playing with words; it's an important difference. It is the children who are the priority now, not the prospective adopters.

That's why the assessment process is so important and intensive. We want to make sure that each child in care finds a permanent family that is right for them. The assessment examines what the prospective adopters can offer a child by looking at their lifestyle, motives, plans, experience of parenting, own childhood, support networks and so on. An important issue today would also be how applicants would handle any contact the child may have with their birth parents or other birth relatives. A sensitive social worker should make the assessment process feel like an exploration, not an interrogation.

What would we urge anyone thinking about adoption to consider? Well, certainly the success stories of adoption. Speak to glowing adoptive parents who will testify how fulfilling adoption can be to all concerned.

And we really do need more adopters. Please consider it. Don't leave those children standing.

Leigh Chambers, Press Officer, British Agencies for Adoption & Fostering

Gay parenting: Adoption
by **Lisa Saffron**

W hen a lesbian or gay couple adopt or foster children together, neither partner has any biological connection to the children. They are beginning their family on a potentially equal basis with no reason for either parent to have a deeper or stronger bond with the children than the other. As soon as the adoption is finalized, however, only one parent has legal status and the other does not, creating the potential for inequality in their relationships. British law does not allow lesbian or gay couples to adopt children. Single people can adopt and one partner in a lesbian and gay couple is normally approved as the legal parent. The other partner can apply to a court for a residence order granting parental responsibility. Although the 1989 Children's Act says that 'no group should be arbitrarily excluded for consideration as carers', many local authorities and voluntary organizations working with children do not consider lesbian and gay applicants for fostering or adoption.

There is no legal objection to lesbians or gay men adopting children. This was confirmed in a landmark decision in 1997. A nine-year-old girl had been placed with a lesbian couple and had lived with them for two years before the local authority asked the court to free her for adoption by one of the lesbians. At this point, the girl's birth mother opposed the freeing order, arguing that lesbians should not be allowed to adopt children. The birth mother was not in a position to look after the girl and in fact was happy with the girl's progress since living with the lesbian couple. The child was settled, thriving and happy and very much wanted to be adopted. The judge could find no legal reason to refuse the order and confirmed that the law permitted adoption by single people whether living alone, in a heterosexual relationship or in a lesbian or gay relationship.

Chapter 14:
The Future

I always saw myself as a parent with a little baby in my arms. Somehow the fact that babies grow up didn't come into it. Judith

When thinking about having a baby, it is easy to focus on the birth and forget about the 18 or so years of dependency that follow afterwards. Children grow up surprisingly quickly and as each birthday passes you will marvel at how rapidly time marches ahead.

Bringing up a child is a major responsibility as you are helping to shape the attitudes and morality of the next generation. You need to instil senses of love, right, wrong, fair play, justice and social awareness in your child as he or she develops from an infant into an adult.

At present, there is no foundation course to prepare you for parenting, apart from your own experiences as a child, although the Government is suggesting introducing some form of parenting-skills training. Unlike items of modern technology, a baby does not come with a manual and bringing up a child is part instinct, part seat-of-your-pants instinct and part advice from other people, especially your extended family.

Over the last two generations, the concept of the extended family has broken down, however. Rather than grandparents, aunts, uncles, brothers, sisters and cousins living and working in a relatively small locality for most of their life, families are now increasingly mobile and likely to move away from each other. This means that increasing numbers of new parents are isolated from relatives who would traditionally have given advice and help with child rearing.

There are a number of questions to ask yourself, such as:

- Do you want to be a liberal parent, or a strict disciplinarian?
- Do you and your partner agree on how your child will be reared?
- Do you want to stay at home until your child reaches school age or later?

- Do you want to return to work as soon as possible?
- What sort of schooling do you wish for your child?
- Can you afford, or even agree with, the principle of private education?
- Are there good schools in your area?
- Do you need to put your child's name down now for the pre-school nursery or schools you hope your child will attend when older?
- What religion will your child be brought up in, if any? Is this something you need to discuss with your partner beforehand?

A variety of good parenting books are available, and it is worth reading at least a few when you start on your quest to have a baby in order to help you answer questions such as these.

Breaking up

Sadly, divorce and separation are becoming more and more common. While children in a single-parent family may be just as loved, happy, secure and stable as those in two-parent families, they are less likely to learn, from close observation, how the dynamics of a long-term mother-father relationship works, especially if the parental break-up is acrimonious.

Bringing up a child is expensive (see chapter 6). New Government guidelines on maintenance payments suggest that an absent parent contributes 15 percent of take-home income towards the cost of rearing a single child, 20 percent for two children, and 25 percent for three or more. This gives a rough estimate of the long-term costs you are likely to be faced with if, as a parent, you abandon the family home leaving your partner to bring up the kids. While few would-be parents would contemplate having a child if they thought they were going to break up, some couples do decide to have a baby in an attempt to patch up a troubled relationship.

> When my wife moved out, taking the children with her, I really missed the positive points about being a father, like waking in the morning and listening to the sounds of children running round the house.
> George, Families Need Fathers

Special needs

Some babies develop into children with special needs. While you cannot predict these when thinking about having a baby, it is worth a passing thought on how you would cope with this. A number of self-help organizations are able to help you should you find yourself in this situation.

A professional on ...
Autism

Autism cannot be identified during prenatal screening. The parents of a child with Down's syndrome, for instance, have their hopes for a 'normal' child shattered from day one, whereas the parents of an autistic child don't suspect a thing until the child is much older – usually by his or her second or third birthday.

Autism is a developmental disorder that robs a child of the ability to communicate effectively, impairs speech, social awareness and play skills. Brain dysfunction is at the core of this devastating condition. Although there are many theories about the cause (or causes) leading to the development of autism, formal research is still inconclusive. To date, there is no known cure for this condition.

Our son Johnathan was three years old when the diagnosis was made. We knew something had gone horribly wrong long before the consultant gave us the diagnosis. Our once happy and sociable child had deteriorated into a clumsy, aggressive bundle of energy, sleeping less than five hours each day! It was just as well that I didn't have to go out to work. His behaviour became erratic, happy one minute and awash with tears the next. He had temper tantrums regularly and seemed oblivious to people around him. To make matters even worse, many so-called friends and older family members made insensitive remarks implying we were inept parents.

There is far more support and understanding for the parents of a child who looks handicapped. Autistic children are usually fine looking and physically well built, belying the fact that they have a profound disability.

We'd like to pay special tribute to a very caring Consultant Paediatrician, Dr Frank Hinde at the Princess Royal Hospital in Shropshire, who counselled us like a trusted friend during the traumatic days surrounding the diagnosis. He advised us to ensure that we made time for each other as a couple. He knew that the arrival of a handicapped child places severe pressure on a couple's relationship. We took his advice and after nearly 14 years our marriage is a happy and beautiful partnership.

We also coped by seeking out others in a similar situation. It is a liberating feeling to know that you can pour out your heart to someone and they fully understand all the issues.

One organization which continues to provide first-rate support for families and training for professionals is the Society for the Autistically Handicapped (SFTAH) based in Kettering, Northamptonshire. It's this support which enabled us to salvage our shattered hopes and battered self-confidence from the tragedy of our son's handicap. My husband changed careers, completing his Masters Degree in Special Needs. He is now fully involved in Parent Support and Advocacy work, offering valuable input both as a parent and a professional.

Perhaps one of the saddest questions that haunts us is, 'What will happen to our son when we die or can no longer cope?' It's only by actively seeking out information, planning and taking the necessary action as soon as possible that any real answer can be found.

Marjorie Burke from the Society for the Autistically Handicapped

Parents often worry about the intelligence of their future child, and whether one who was highly intelligent would be too much for them to cope with.

A professional on ...
Coping with an unusually gifted child

'Giftedness' or high ability is partly genetic. You may be able to guess whether you are likely to have a very able baby or not. Think of the life profile of your family, whether there are people who are talented, have an unusual grasp of a topic, or have been very successful. Equally, think of bright family members who have met resistance, achieved little and felt frustrated. The second contributory factor is upbringing. If you have a gifted child, you will need to be on your toes, for this child will wear you out with questions.

There will be many joys with your gifted child, but perhaps some worries too. You may find your boy or girl waking early, beginning to venture on words and sentences before he or she is a year old. She may well learn to read early and soon ask difficult questions like 'How did the world start?' On the other hand many very bright children sleep rather badly, their minds refusing to switch off even in the dark.

A considerable number of bright or gifted children are aggressive as toddlers, frustrated as they are because they cannot grow up quickly enough. They learn to switch the TV on and off, but it takes longer to find the right buttons to start and stop the video. They want to do these things immediately, and lose patience when they can't. The neighbours will initially look at these children and say 'Isn't she bright!' and you will feel proud. But soon they will be comparing them to their own children and so your child will attract envy.

The playgroup is important for gifted children. The leaders will need to understand that your child wants to look at books as well as play with toys: very able children don't see a difference between 'play' and learning, and in fact most learning comes through 'play' – trying things out to see what happens.

Some schools are excellent in the way they deal with able children, with a policy in place to enable such children to progress at their own natural speeds. But you may be unlucky and find a school where bright children are unwanted. When this happens, teachers may try to pretend they are not bright, or that this is a matter of no importance, and not the true centre of your child's personality. Some schools are upset if children don't relate well to their age peers, and want the child to be 'socialized' before he/she can be allowed to learn. This undermines the child's confidence and depresses the likelihood that social interaction will be harmonious; bullying or neglect may even result. In this respect there is no difference between 'state' schools and the independent sector. Some schools in each sector are good, some bad.

Gifted children love to learn, and feel miserable when this is a low priority at school. Sometimes they can appear bossy or cheeky, but this is usually not intentional. They like teachers with a sense of humour, who will sometimes treat them as real people and not patronise them. If things are going badly, they may pretend not to care, or switch off. They may find writing difficult, and if criticized, they may dry up. They hate being bored by repetitious and unintelligent tasks. They can safely be trusted to work by themselves or in small groups, so they need be no trouble to the teacher at all, but if they are badly treated they will revolt and cause mayhem.

Very able and gifted children may have a speciality they particularly enjoy, but they should be given every opportunity to try as wide a curriculum as possible. Unfortunately, neglect by the system sometimes turns these children into withdrawn or disruptive people, bitterly disappointed or even suicidal. Parents can provide the security and encouragement they need, but it may be demanding and time-consuming. If you do conceive a gifted child, you can be well blessed, but don't expect to have time on your hands!

Edward Chitham, MA PhD, FRSA the National Association for Gifted Children

Of all the questions potential parents ask themselves before deciding to have a baby, the sexual orientation of their child is probably near the bottom of the list, if it makes the list at all.

A professional on ...
Coming to terms with your child's sexuality

What a big decision it can be – I want to have a baby, but ... there are so many questions one asks of oneself, one's partner and the professionals. Nevertheless, in the beginning, one question rarely asked is, 'Will it be heterosexual?' You mean you never thought of that – neither did I – or my partner, or the professionals! Only 16 years later were my husband and I presented with the fact. Where do you go with the questions that pour into your mind at such times?

I remember joining a group of non-heterosexuals one late afternoon in the centre of Leeds to collect signatures for a petition on some legal matter concerning inequality of lesbian, gay and bisexual people. It was an extremely cold and wet day and it quickly fell dark as the offices began to empty and shoppers rushed home. We approached everyone who 'looked' a possible person to be on our list (I've no idea how we worked this out). One of my targets was laden with parcels, bags and had two small children in tow. I dashed after her and asked, 'Excuse me – but do you realize you may find that one of your children is gay?' She glared at me, held the children's hands firmly and with a backward glance screamed, 'At this moment I don't b— care!' I often wonder if she ever thinks of that and has begun to actually ask herself or her children this question some ten years on.

When I see a little baby being pushed along the road, or in the supermarket trolley, I (and many like me), more often wonder what sexuality the child has, rather than whether it is a boy or a girl. If we'd thought of this while our own children were babies – or even before we chose pregnancy as an option – we may have dwelt on the decision-making much longer. We may have considered the pros and cons, the whys and wherefores and the shall I/ shan't I of the situation.

Neither my husband nor I had ever considered our children as different in any way from other children; they were children who would grow up to be adults. They would, of course, have partners of the opposite sex and eventually marry. And, given time, there would be grandchildren.

These are the expectations that most parents, looking back, will have had. Never once did I consider or imagine the children were other than heterosexual.

Our eldest son was very clever at school; his O- and A-levels were excellent. Our youngest son was quite good at school with reasonable O- and A - levels. He had lots of problems there though and we couldn't seem to find out what these were. He, too, was obviously puzzled and wasn't able to say exactly why this was happening. He would arrive home with bruises right up the fronts of his legs, which I eventually found to be from a much bigger boy kicking him. There was the theft of his lunch-box and his books would go missing. This was our quiet, pleasant son who worked hard and seemed to be reasonably easy-going, but always very 'serious' and quiet.

The time came when he had nightmares and couldn't (or wouldn't) let us know what they were about. He became worried about a 'treat' swimming lesson even though he loved swimming. Then one day he sat in my car and said, 'It's happened': he was asthmatic and he'd been held under the water by a person or persons unknown and had to be revived. The worry of it all became so great that we didn't know where to turn – receiving little help from his schools over the years.

He continued to do well with his lessons – so the worries we experienced seemed to be unfounded, yet they 'niggled'.

Then the day came when, on his way home from school, he said he had something to tell me – 'in my own time'. Off I went, worrying yet again, until he came downstairs, sat opposite me with a strange look on his face and said: 'Two of your friends will understand.' It took quite some time for me to hit on which two friends – a gay couple.

That's that! We'd never thought of it, never even considered it. Our son was gay and he'd struggled quite alone with this knowledge for at least four years (from around 12 years of age) and we'd had no idea whatsoever – not an inkling of his long and lonely internal upheaval. This will always be the saddest part for me, his mother. I gathered him in my arms and told him he was still the same person he'd been two minutes earlier and it made no difference. It was so obviously a great relief to him. For us, it solved many problems. I'd said all the right things, but didn't realize it until much later; but I'd meant it – and still do.

Gradually, our lives changed drastically as we realized there was little or nothing in the way of support for parents in our situation. Some were traumatized by their child coming out, others devastated. We decided to use our home telephone number as a 'helpline'. Very soon we realized callers were asking to be put in touch with others, which was not possible as all calls were confidential and we needed to take personal details. So, the Parents' Friend Helpline became an organization and not just a helpline. We began to run monthly meetings for parents and other family members affected by a loved one's 'coming out'. We produced literature to help 'educate' our 'members' and callers. My husband and I had always believed in equality before we ever realized the inequality in law where our lesbian, gay and bisexual children were, and still are, concerned. We marched the marches, flew our banners and became quite 'political'.

We would not wish to change or go back on any part of it. We have no regrets at having a gay son. Our minds and heart have not only been blown open but have exploded into an understanding and love of a whole new way of being.

So, when you begin to feel broody, thinking, 'I want a baby', be forewarned and, as they say, forearmed in the knowledge that your baby may grow up to be an adult but not in the way you thought. Never have expectations of your children.

Joy Dickens, Co-founder of Parents' Friend

Appendix II:
A professional on ...
Trade secrets

1 Pregnancy is not a disease but usually a very healthy state – the clinic and hospital visits are just a precaution.

2 Invest in an answer machine to filter calls asking, 'Has it happened yet?' or you'll soon run out of polite ways of saying 'No!'

3 To avoid impatience, remember from the start that the baby may well be born at least 41 weeks, not the 40 used as the 'due date'.

4 The average delivery date for the first baby is 40 weeks and five days, so remember while some will arrive before then, as many will be born after.

5 The second pregnancy is usually the easiest of all. If you had a vaginal delivery first time it's almost guaranteed to be easier second time round. As my obstetric boss used to put it, 'If you had your first vaginally, you can have your second behind a hedge in Richmond Park.'

Dr Alex Bobak, GP.

Conclusion

Having had a baby, you will now obviously have to rear him or her to the best of your ability. You will need to form strong views on how you want your child to learn right from wrong, whether discipline will involve physical smacking or whether punishments will be verbal and involve removal of favourite toys or denial of treats. How you yourself were reared will play a large part in your parenting behaviour. Some people find themselves copying their own parents while others go out of their way to do things differently for their own children. Whatever approach you take to parenting, remember that children have to push at your boundaries in order to learn the limits of acceptable behaviour. It is important to maintain consistency and for both parents to back each other up.

There are many excellent parenting books available – once your baby has arrived, make sure you read one or two. Your baby doesn't arrive with his own manual, and to a certain extent good parenting is an instinctive skill. By reading what respected professionals advise however, you can improve your chances of being the best parent your child could possibly have had.

Appendix 1:

What newcomers to Britain need to know about having a baby

Some people wanting to become parents have additional issues to think about linked to their religious and cultural backgrounds. Dr Bashir Qureshi, an expert on transcultural medicine, offers the following advice for would-be parents from different ethnic backgrounds.

1 Understand the British Healthcare and Social Welfare Systems

Visit your general practitioner (GP) and get to know the functions of the GP, practice nurse, health visitor, midwife, practice manager and receptionists and find out which services are available at the practice. See the health visitor attached to that practice to discuss all your plans, hopes and anxieties about having a baby. A health visitor is the specialist nurse dealing with children under five and their parents. A midwife will help you during the pregnancy (antenatal), delivery (natal) and after delivery (postnatal) periods. A midwife will visit you until the tenth day after delivery from which time your child's healthcare will be handed over to a health visitor. Although health visitors mainly supervise the care of the child from birth to the age of five years, they have now extended their role to give preconception advice and to run antenatal classes in which the participation of both parents is encouraged. A health visitor will also inform you about the services available from other health professionals and workers in the local social services department.

Visit your local social security department and also your local social services department. To find out what grants, aids, support, maternity leave privileges and other facilities are available. If you foresee any financial or accommodation problems, feel free to inform the social worker who will be able to help you. Such assistance should not be construed as charity handouts or akin to begging, which is so common and detested in many developing countries. In Britain, society shares the responsibility of childcare with the parents. In Eastern societies, the upbringing of a child, including education, is solely the parents' responsibility but in Western societies the parents have to share this privilege with other citizens such as health professionals and social workers. This concept is woven into the fabric of British law.

If you are new to Britain it is essential that you learn about the British way of life and work, the National Health Service and social services systems. Over a period of time you will pick this all up, from your British-born neighbours, friends and health professionals. In doing so please remember two basic points:

British people are excellent teachers, but they only teach if requested to do so. By their nature, they are independent people who do not want to be told what to do and thus refrain from telling others what to do. Nevertheless, when you need help, do not hesitate to ask. They will tell you what you need to know and more.

British people believe in fair play. People from other cultures have described them as one of the most honest ethnic groups in the world. If you play fair with British citizens, health professionals and social workers, you will find that they will help you all the way from preconception to childbirth and beyond.

2 Follow your culture, but make sure you let the health professionals know about your cultural customs

The British and British-trained health professionals will, hopefully, respect your culture but it is essential that you tell them about any cultural habits which you believe to be related to conception, pregnancy and labour. As Britain becomes more and more multicultural, health professionals are becoming increasingly aware of any innocent cultural distinctions which have medical implications.

Cousin marriages are common in the Eastern culture, particularly among Arabs and Asians. The aim of such marriages is to preserve the family name and honour;.it also provides financial security for the bride in the extended family system where an arranged marriage is the norm. However, according to medical research, there is a possibility that a child born of a cousin marriage may develop congenital abnormalities. It is also possible that an early pregnancy may result in miscarriage. If you let your doctor or health visitor know about your situation, they will arrange screening for foetal abnormalities in early pregnancy and advise accordingly.

'Hot and cold food' is an Eastern concept which is especially popular in the Middle East, Africa and on the Indian subcontinent. Broadly speaking, all kinds of meat are considered 'hot' and all fruit juices and milk are considered 'cold'. According to Eastern custom, 'hot' food should be avoided in pregnancy and 'cold' food should be avoided in all cases of respiratory infections. The scientific explanation is that protein foods ('hot') accelerate the intestinal blood flow and increase the absorption of food and any bacteria or allergy causing allergens with it. Of course, the absorption of any drug, including antibiotics, is speeded up. On the other hand, starchy foods ('cold') will have the reverse effect. Women in the Eastern cultures are advised not to eat meat in pregnancy. In addition, the majority of Hindus are vegetarians by culture and religion. All these mothers may develop iron deficiency anaemia and other dietary deficiencies or malnutrition. So it is in the interest of all would-be parents to tell their health professionals if they do not eat meat. After a blood test appropriate supplements of drugs and diet will be advised. The doctor or midwife will also give the mother-to-be a folic acid supplement to take before conception and up to 12 weeks of pregnancy (see page 117).

3 Worship according to your religion, but inform the health professionals about religious rituals

Fasting is a ritual in almost all religions. However in Islam an entire month every year called Ramadan is dedicated to dawn-to-dusk fasting, where there is total prohibition of food and drink intake. This ritual has high spiritual benefits. However, during the fast, a person's blood sugar falls. Usually this transient fall of blood sugar is harmless but it can lead to headaches or weakness. It is essential that both would-be parents, particularly the mother, are free from any disease if they are to fast. It is also prudent that you inform your health professionals – doctor or nurse – about fasting. This information may also be relevant to any required drug treatment or preconception folic acid supplements.

Prayers, too, are a vital part of all religions. Scientifically, these are based on spiritual enrichment, physical exercise, meditation and relaxation. All these components in every prayer do have beneficial effects. However, some effects may have medical consequences. For example, the blood pressure falls considerably during meditation and this fall, which is temporary, may be enough to make a blood pressure reading in a normal person less reliable, and may affect drug treatment in a patient who actually suffers from high blood pressure. Therefore, it is wise to inform the doctor, practice nurse or midwife of all these prayers and any other religious rituals you think might affect your health assessment or influence any exercise or medicine prescribed by a doctor or suggested by other health professionals.

Religious symbols, charms, bracelets and holy water are often used within religion to safeguard health and to avert accidents, disease or misfortune. All these are provided by the religious leaders or healers in good faith and they induce a sense of security and self-confidence in the recipient. A wedding ring also becomes a symptom of emotional attachment and its removal, even for medical procedures, may be interpreted as a bad omen to the marriage or the partner. Unfortunately, however, in certain circumstances, health professionals will have to remove these holy items. For example, all metal objects on a patient's body must be removed if diathermy apparatus is used in an operation such as a Caesarean section to avoid burns. In other surgery, earrings or bracelets have to be removed before surgery, but wedding rings can be worn covered with a sticky plaster.

Problems may also arise when a patient is wearing or using a holy item to prevent or cure a disease and delays or declines to seek medical advice. Such practice may result in serious consequences. Even at the stage of preconception consultation, it is wise to tell a nurse, midwife or doctor about such the holy items. They might modify their procedures or negotiate the matter with you.

4 Be proud of your ethnic characteristics and ask health professionals if these are relevant to preconception advice

Although every disease may occur in any ethnic group, some diseases have been found to occur more often in certain ethnic groups. Knowing the possible genetic or environmental risks that may apply to you is to your advantage because on many occasions screening, genetic counselling or management are available.

According to current medical research, the following groups are vulnerable to certain genetic conditions:

- Europeans – cystic fibrosis
- European Jews – Tay Sach's disease
- Asians – haemoglobin D Punjab disease
- Africans – sickle cell disease
- Greeks/Cypriots – beta thalassaemia
- Vietnamese – alpha thalassaemia
- Chinese – primary idiopathic acquired aplastic anaemia.

The list is long and almost every ethnic (racial) group carries the risk of having one or more genetic conditions that can affect the child during pregnancy and after birth. Ethnic distinctions are respectable entities in science and these should not be confused with the political terms of discrimination. It is wise to ask health professionals about any potential ethnic genetic risk that might affect your unborn child. They will investigate, screen and advise as appropriate. In some situations, genetic counselling will be arranged at preconception stage for both parents. No would-be parent, or parents, should feel any guilt for belonging to a particular ethnic group. Everyone, but everyone, should feel proud of their ethnic origin. Those would-be parents who are themselves children of mixed marriages should also inform doctors, nurses or midwives of these facts because they may be relevant to conception, pregnancy, labour, puerperium or to the child.

It is also important that both would-be parents inform their health professionals if they suffer, or have suffered in the past, from a disease or infectious condition, including tuberculosis and sexually transmitted diseases such as AIDS and syphilis. This information needs to be considered by doctors in order for them help their patients and the unborn child. Some non-infectious diseases can also affect pregnancy or labour and so should be discussed preconceptually. For example, a disease called systemic lupus erythematosus (SLE), a proven cause of recurrent miscarriage, is three times more common in black women than in whites. Another example is osteomalacia, which causes a bony deformity of the pelvis and can obstruct labour necessitating a Caesarean section, and is common among Asian and African women. It is therefore essential that would-be parents, especially women, see a doctor, midwife, nurse or health visitor when they are planning to have a baby.

5 When you consult others, always tell your health professionals

Self-medication is popular in Britain and abroad. Some medication bought over-the-counter may affect conception, pregnancy or labour favourably or adversely. For example, ergotamine preparations for migraines may cause miscarriage. So, when planning a baby, parents should consult a pharmacist

Alternative or complementary medicine has always been used worldwide and it is becoming increasingly popular in Britain. Some preparations contain herbs which have medicinal properties, and these can diminish, increase or neutralize the effects of some drugs prescribed by the doctor. Therefore, always inform your health professionals of any alternative remedies you may be taking and remember that it is safest not to use alternative medicine and allopathic (conventional) medicine simultaneously.

In the Eastern culture and in some religions, it is desirable to have at least one boy in the family. Some would-be parents from such a background may choose to use pills or compounds which can be obtained, even by mail order, from some practitioners of alternative medicine such as Hakims (Muslim healers) and Vaids (Hindu healers). For genuine reasons, these may contain potent herbs or metal compounds. But some of these may have toxic effects when their recommended dose is exceeded. It is best to double check with the practitioners who provided these remedies, counter-check with a pharmacist in Britain and tell your doctor, midwife or nurse that you are using them.

Voluntary organizations do much good work in the UK. There are many societies and self-help groups which give advice on one genetic or ethnically specific disease or problem – for example, sickle cell disease, Tay Sach's, thalassaemia, cystic fibrosis and so on. You can obtain their addresses and telephone numbers from your health visitor, practice nurse, practice manager, local librarian and telephone directories (see also Resources, pages 238-241). Such organisations are largely funded by donations, but their advice to clients is usually free of charge. However you should inform your health professionals if you are following the advice of any of these voluntary agencies.

Dr Bashir Qureshi is the author of *Transcultural Medicine: Dealing with patients from different cultures, religions and ethnicities* (Petroc Press)

A professional on ...
Trade secrets

1 Pregnancy is not a disease but usually a very healthy state – the clinic and hospital visits are just a precaution.

2 Invest in an answer machine to filter calls asking, 'Has it happened yet?' or you'll soon run out of polite ways of saying 'No!'

3 To avoid impatience, remember from the start that the baby may well be born at least 41 weeks, not the 40 used as the 'due date'.

4 The average delivery date for the first baby is 40 weeks and five days, so remember while some will arrive before then, as many will be born after.

5 The second pregnancy is usually the easiest of all. If you had a vaginal delivery first time it's almost guaranteed to be easier second time round. As my obstetric boss used to put it, 'If you had your first vaginally, you can have your second behind a hedge in Richmond Park.'

Dr Alex Bobak, GP.

Appendix III:
Resources

General

Active Birth Centre
25 Bickerton Road
London N19 4JT
Tel: 0171-561 9006
Fax: 0171-561 9007
e-mail:
mail@activebirthcentr.demon.co.uk
Website: www.activebirthcentre.com

Helps prospective parents achieve an optimum pregnancy and labour by exploring alternatives and increasing awareness of the benefits of active birth and breast-feeding. Provides information on active birth, yoga, baby massage and gymnastics plus a variety of alternative therapies, including homoeopathy and acupuncture. Can provide water pools for birth.

Association for Post-Natal Illness
25 Jerdan Place
London SW6 1BE
Tel: 0171-386 0868
Fax: 0171-386 8885

Provides support to mothers suffering from postnatal illness, works to increase public awareness of the condition and to encourage research into its cause and nature.

Fertility UK
Clitherow House
1 Blythe Mews
London W14 0NW
Tel: 0171-371 1341
Fax: 0171-371 4921
e-mail: admin@fertilityUK.org
Website: http://www.fertilityUK.org

National Fertility Awareness & Natural Family Planning Service is an independent service of Marriage Care. Fertility UK is funded by the Department of Health to provide evidence-based fertility awareness information, educational materials about fertility awareness and natural family planning. The main focus of the service is to help couples planning a pregnancy understand how fertility works – particularly to understand the main signs of fertility. Provides a referral service to accredited fertility awareness teachers and comprehensive training for health professionals in fertility awareness and natural family planning.

Maternity Alliance
45 Beech Street
London EC2P 2LX
Tel: 0171-588 8582 (advice line)
Fax: 0171-588 8584

Helps to improve health care, social and financial support and the legal rights of parents-to-be and families during the first year of a baby's life. Funds research, seminars and campaigns on maternity issues. Supplies information and leaflets.

Meet-a-Mum-Association (MAMA)
14 Willis Road
Croydon CR0 2XX
Tel: 0181-771 5595
Fax: 0181-665 1972

Supports mothers of young children and those with postnatal depression. Organizes social meetings, lectures, baby-sitting and practical 'mother-to-mother' support for those who are isolated, lonely or depressed. Promotes research.

Multiple Births Foundation (MBF)
Queen Charlotte's and Chelsea Hospital
Goldhawk Road
London W6 0XG
Tel: 0181-383 3519
Fax: 0181-383 3041
e-mail: mbf@rpms.ac.uk

Provides professional support for families with multiple births. Organizes clinics for multiple birth families in London, evening meetings for parents and provides literature and an advisory service to parents and professionals.

National Childbirth Trust (NCT)
Alexandra House
Oldham Terrace
London W3 6NH
Tel: 0181-992 8637 (helpline 9.30am-4.30pm)
Fax: 0181-992 5929

Offers information and support in pregnancy, childbirth and early parenthood, to enable all parents to make informed choices. Provides antenatal classes, breast-feeding counselling, postnatal support and birth/parenthood education in schools. Also runs support groups for parents with disabilities and those having miscarriages and Caesareans. Provides a number of information leaflets, including Making a Birth Plan, Postnatal Depression, Breast-feeding: Returning to Work, Where shall I have my baby? and Becoming a Dad.

Tommy's Campaign
1 Kennington Road
London SE1 7RR
Tel: 0171-620 0188
Fax: 0171-928 6628

Tommy's Campaign is the only UK charity to focus exclusively on research into the causes of problems in pregnancy such as miscarriage, premature birth and stillbirth. Since it was set up in 1992 the charity has become established as a leading light in foetal research. The charity has appointed its own Professor of Foetal Health, based at St Thomas' Hospital in London, who has set up a dedicated research team working on 37 medical research projects at hospitals and universities throughout the country.

One of the charity's most important aims is to inform mothers-to-be of ways to ensure a healthy pregnancy and to provide the unborn baby with the best possible start. Tommy's Campaign works with health professionals in helping to distribute advice to women on all aspects of pregnancy through GP surgeries, health centres and antenatal clinics. Women can also contact the charity directly for information on research and the latest developments in antenatal care.

Some of the research projects which have been funded by the charity are beginning to mature into trials which may, when completed, have a major impact on antenatal care. For instance, the PREMET trial was launched nationally in June 1998. This trial hopes to establish whether a drug, Metronidazole, can help in preventing preterm labour by countering infection in the uterus. It is thought that infection, when left untreated, can cause the onset of premature labour. The trial needs to recruit at least 4,000 women, who are considered to be at risk of premature birth. It is expected to last two years and is open to women throughout the UK, when referred to PREMET by their GP or obstetrician.

For further details on PREMET please phone 0171-922 8094.

Twins & Multiple Births Association (TAMBA)

PO Box 30
Little Sutton
South Wirral L66 1TH
Tel: 0870-121 4000; 01732-868000
TAMBA Twinline (helpline weekdays
7-11pm, Sat-Sun 10am-11pm)
Fax: 0870-121 4001

*Provides information and mutual support networks
for families of twins, triplets and more and all those
involved in their care. Promotes greater
understanding of the needs of multiple birth
families by publishing and distributing material on
topics of interest. Encourages research into the
health, social and educational needs of twins,
triplets and more. Provides opportunities for
members to meet and maintains contact with local
twins clubs. Maintains specialist support services
such as bereavement, one-parent families, special
needs, super twins (triplets or more), multiple births
through fertility treatment, adult twins and the
Twinline helpline.*

WellBeing, The Health Research Charity for Women and Babies

27 Sussex Place
Regent's Park
London NW1 4SP
Tel: 0171-262 5337
Fax: 0171-724 7725

*WellBeing is the research arm of the Royal College
of Obstetricians and Gynaecologists. It funds medical
and scientific research in hospitals and universities
around the UK into all matters of women's health,
as well as the health of newborn babies.*

Sainsbury's/WellBeing Eating for Pregnancy Helpline

Tel: 0114-242 4084 (Mon-Fri 10am-4pm
plus out of hours answerphone).

*Offers nutritional advice for women planning a
pregnancy, pregnant women and women who are
breast-feeding.*

Problems in Pregnancy

British Diabetic Association (BDA)

10 Queen Anne Street
London W1M 0BD
Tel: 0171-636 6112 (Careline)
Fax: 0171-637 3644

*Provides support for those with diabetes and others
interested in it; promotes a greater understanding of
the condition through research and education.
Provides a wide range of information literature and
videos; organizes educational and activity holidays
for children with diabetes. Runs the 'Tadpole Club'
for children.*

British Epilepsy Association (BEA)

Anstey House
40 Hanover Square
Leeds LS3 1BE
Tel: 0800-309030 (Freephone national
helpline)
Fax: 0113-242 8804

*Promotes increased public awareness and
understanding of epilepsy by providing information
and advice and through research into the condition.
Provides advice, information and support for people
with epilepsy and local help through a national
network of self-help groups or branches.*

Myalgic Encephalomyelitis (ME) Association

Stanhope House
High Street
Stanhope-le-Hope
Essex SS17 0HA
Tel: 01375-361013
Fax: 01375-360256

*Raises awareness of ME and provides help and
information for sufferers through local groups and a
phone helpline.*

National Osteoporosis Society

PO Box 10
Radstock
Bath BA3 3YB
Tel: 01761-472721 (helpline 9.30am-4.30pm)
Fax: 01761-471104

Raises awareness of all aspects of osteoporosis and related conditions; provides information; helps sufferers by letter and phone, newsletters, publications and local groups; funds research.

PMS Help

PO Box 83
Hereford HR4 8YQ

Helps sufferers of pre-menstrual syndrome, postnatal illness and other related hormonal illnesses. Provides literature. Postal enquiries only.

Attention X Medical Hair Design

316 King Street
Hammersmith
London
W6 0RR
Tel: 0181-741 8224

Medical hair design specialists who are able to advise on all types of hair loss, including that after pregnancy. Bald patches can, in most cases, be disguised with hair-like fibres as long as you have a small amount of natural hair on which to lock the design.

Problems with Offspring

Association for Children with Life-threatening or Terminal Conditions and Their Families (ACT)

65 St Michael's Hill
Bristol BS2 8DZ
Tel: 0117-922 1556 Mon-Fri 8.30-4.30 (answerphone at other times)
Fax: 0117-930 4707   .

ACT campaigns on behalf of families caring for children with life-threatening or terminal conditions to encourage the development of children's palliative care services. Promotes models of good care and provides information for families and professionals working with them. ACT produces several publications including an information pack on children's hospices.

Association for Spina Bifida and Hydrocephalus (ASBAH)

42 Park Road
Peterborough PE1 2UQ
Tel: 01733-555988
Fax: 01733-555985
website: www.asbah.demon.co.uk

Has a network of specialist staff who provide advice, support and advocacy for people with spina bifida and/or hydrocephalus, and their carers. Promotes their interests and their successful integration into society.

Cancer and Leukaemia in Childhood Trust (UK) (CLIC UK)

12-13 King Square
Bristol BS2 8JH
Tel: 0117-924 8844
Fax: 0117-924 4505

Helps to alleviate the suffering and distress of children with cancer and leukaemia and their families. Offers welfare grants and 'crisis break' accommodation to sick children and has developed regional networks of domiciliary care nurses and 'homes from home', for families to stay near their sick children in hospital.

Children's Information Centre

Hampton Grange
21 Hampton Lane
Solihull
W Midlands B91 2QJ
Tel: 0121-705 4547
Fax: 0121-705 4547

Promotes increased awareness of the needs of gifted and talented children. Offers free telephone counselling; arranges psychological assessments for gifted, dyslexic, left-handed children and those with handicaps.

Provides legal advice to help parents in their negotiations with schools and school authorities.

Congenital CMV Association
69 The Leasowes
Ford
Shrewsbury SY5 9LU
Tel: 01743-850055

Promotes greater awareness of congenital cytomegalovirus and supports affected families. Runs parent self-help support groups and provides advice and information.

Contact a Family
170 Tottenham Court Road
London W1P 0HA
Tel: 0171-383 3555
Fax: 0171-383 0259

Promotes mutual support between families caring for children with any type of disability or special need within the same neighbourhood. Encourages the formation of parent support groups at local, regional and national levels of which over 800 have been formed. Runs a national helpline for parents and professionals.

Cot Death Society
1 Browning Close
Thatcham
Berks RG18 3EF
Tel: 01635-861771
Fax: 01635-861771

Promotes increased awareness of cot death, and helps to preserve the lives of those at risk by providing respiration monitors, together with training, backup and support. Runs an information service for parents and healthcare professionals.

Cystic Fibrosis Trust
Alexandra House
5 Blyth Road
Bromley BR1 3RS
Tel: 0181-464 7211
Fax: 0181-313 0472

Promotes research into CF and the establishment of groups throughout the UK to help and advise people with CF and their families; works to increase awareness of the condition and early diagnosis in young children. A network of 300 branches and

groups advise CF families with problems arising in schooling, employment, holidays, housing etc.

Down's Syndrome Association
155 Mitcham Road
London SW17 9PG
Tel: 0181-682 4001 (24-hour helpline)
Fax: 0181-682 4012

Promotes the care and education of persons with Down's Syndrome, and supports research into the condition. Acts as a parents' self-help organization which encourages the formation of branches and groups throughout the UK.

Foundation for the Study of Infant Deaths/Cot Death Research and Support (FSID)
14 Halkin Street
London SW1X 7DP
Tel: 0171-235 0965 (general enquiries); 0171-235 1721(24-hour helpline); 0171-823 2216 (appeals)
Fax: 0171-823 1986

Promotes research into the causes and prevention of sudden infant death syndrome, and supports/counsels bereaved parents, both centrally and through local groups.

Genetic Interest Group (GIG)
Farringdon Point
29-35 Farringdon Road
London EC1M 3JB
Tel: 0171-430 0090
Fax: 0171-430 0092

Promotes increased awareness of human genetic disorders and their impact on all those affected by them. Promotes access to information, advice, support, counselling and treatment for all those affected. Provides an information helpline and postal information service.

Hyperactive Children's Support Group
71 Whyke Lane
Chichester
W Sussex PO19 2LD
Tel: 01903-725182 (10am-1pm)
Fax: 01903-725182

Provides help and support for hyperactive children and their families. Promotes research into the condition, its causes and treatment plus gives dietary advice.

Miscarriage Association
c/o Clayton Hospital
Northgate
Wakefield
W Yorkshire WF1 3JS
Tel: 01924-200799
Fax: 01924-298834

Provides support and information on miscarriage, ectopic pregnancy and moal pregnancy. Co-ordinates a UK-wide network of telephone contacts and support groups, publishes a range of leaflets, encourages good practice in hospitals and GP surgeries and raises public awareness of the issues around pregnancy loss.

National Association for Gifted Children
Elder House
Milton Keynes
MK9 1LR
Tel: 01908-673677
Fax: 01908-673679
e-mail: nagc@rmplc.co.uk

Helps to develop gifts and talents in children. Promotes the welfare and needs of gifted children, their parents and families. Provides a voluntary counselling service and self-help for parents, plus activities for children.

SCOPE
12 Park Crescent
London W1 4EQ
Tel: 0800-626216 (Freefone Cerebral Palsy helpline Mon-Fri 9am-9pm, Sat, Sun 2-6pm)
Fax: 0171-436 2601

Works to enable those with cerebral palsy to achieve maximum independence and personal fulfilment. Has a network of over 200 local support groups in England and Wales, and has established schools, education centres, units and residential centres. Provides a confidential helpline for counselling and information on cerebral palsy and related disabilities.

Sick Children's Trust
1a Doughty Street
London WC1N 2PH
Tel: 0171-404 3329
Fax: 0171-831 3182

Works to alleviate the stress of families whose child require hospital treatment for a life-threatening illness far from home, by providing accommodation. Projects so far have been established in London, Kent and Yorkshire.

Society for the Autistically Handicapped (SFTAH)
199-201 Blandford Avenue
Kettering
Northants NN16 9AT
Tel: 01536-523274
Fax: 01536-523274

Promotes increased awareness of sufferers and their needs, as well as helping to alleviate the stress of carers. Provides a 24-hour help- and advice-line.

STEPS – National Association for Children with Congenital Abnormalities
15 Statham Close
Lymm
Cheshire WA13 9NN
Tel: 01925-757525 (Mon-Sat 10am-4pm; Sun 11am-2pm)
Fax: 01925-753913

Provides support and information for families of children born with lower limb abnormalities. Puts families in touch with each other through the STEPS Contact Register.

Stillbirth and Neonatal Death Society (SANDS)
28 Portland Place
London W1N 4DE
Tel: 0171-436 5881 (helpline)
Fax: 0171-436 3715

Offers support to parents bereaved through late pregnancy loss, stillbirth or neonatal death. Encourages increased awareness of the needs of bereaved families. Has established over 200 local self-help groups and contacts.

Support Around Termination for Abnormality (SATFA)
73 Charlotte Street
London W1P 1LB
Tel: 0171-631 0285 (helpline)
Fax: 0171-631 0280

Provides support and information to parents through antenatal testing, and when an abnormality is diagnosed in their unborn baby. Continued support is offered to those parents who choose to end the pregnancy.

SENSE: The National Deafblind and Rubella Association
11-13 Clifton Terrace
London N4 3SR
Tel: 0181-991 0513 (Family Advisory Service helpline for children under seven)
Tel: 0171-272 7774 (head office)
Fax: 0171-272 6012

Promotes increased services for children who were born deafblind as a result of rubella. To work for the benefit of dual sensory impaired and sensory impaired multiply disabled children and adults. Provides advice, support and information for families and has organized a regional network of self-help groups. Promotes the improved uptake of immunization against major childhood diseases, including Rubella.

Toxoplasmosis Trust
61-71 Collier Street
London N1 9BE
Tel: 0171-713 0599 (helpline)
Fax: 0171-713 0611
e-mail: ttt@toxo.org.uk

Promotes greater awareness of toxoplasmosis and provides support for sufferers and their families. Provides an advice service for pregnant women, sufferers, their families and promotes research into all aspects of the illness. A variety of leaflets and fact sheets are available.

Breast-feeding

Association of Breast-feeding Mothers (ABM)
PO Box 207
Bridgewater
TA6 7YT
Tel: 0171-813 1481
E-mail: abm@clara.net
Website: hhtp://home.clara.net/abm/

Promotes increased awareness of the benefits of breast-feeding and how to do it.. Runs a telephone counselling service.

La Leche League of Great Britain
Box BM 3424
London WC1N 3XX
Tel: 0171-242 1278

Provides information, support and personal help to women who wish to breast-feed their babies through mother-to mother support groups and a telephone helpline.

Parenthood

Serene and the CRY-SIS helpline
London WC1N 3XX
Tel: 0171-4045011 (8am-11pm)

Provides information, emotional support and practical advice to parents of babies who cry incessantly and have sleep problems, and of older children with problems such as temper tantrums, clinging and long-term crying. Offers information about possible causes of such behaviour. Publications available – send stamped addressed envelope, please.

PARENTLINE
Endway House
The Endway
Hadleigh
Essex SS7 2AN
Tel: 01702-554782 (admin); 01702-559900 (helpline)
Fax: 01702-554911

Provides support for parents under stress to maximize a family's capacity to care and reduce the incidence of child abuse and neglect.

PRAMS – Information and Support to Parents
Churchgate House
96 Churchgate
Stockport
Cheshire SK1 1YJ
Tel: 0161-477 0606 (Mon-Thurs 9am-4.45pm; Fri 9.30am-2pm)
Fax: 0161-477 0606

Provides information and support for parents and self-help groups concerned with families. Aims to establish contact and understanding between everyone seeking to help parents. Runs a phone helpline and free daytime counselling.

Parents Anonymous London (PAL)
Manor Gardens Centre
6-9 Manor Gardens
London N7 6LA
Tel: 0171-263 8918 (7pm-12 midnight most evenings)

Offers friendship and help to those parents who are tempted to abuse their child and those who have done so.

Parents' Friend
c/o Voluntary Action Leeds
Stringer House
34 Lupton Street
Leeds LS10 2QW
Tel: 0113-267 4627 (8-10pm)

Provides counselling and support for parents, relatives and friends of gay, lesbian and bisexual children, through face-to-face and phone counselling and a support group.

Exploring Parenthood
4 Ivory Place
20a Treadgold Street
London W11 4BP
Tel: 0171-221 6681 (parents' advice line)
Fax: 0171-221 5501

Works to prevent stress and breakdown in family life through a one-stop parents' support service to help with minor worries or major concerns. Runs a parents' advice line and group counselling sessions.

Family Crisis Line
1 York Road
Woking
Surrey GU22 7QQ
Tel: 01483-722533 (10am-10pm)

Provides a confidential, sympathetic ear for callers wishing to talk about any form of domestic crisis or situation that causes them stress.

Mothers' Union (MU)
The Mary Sumner House
24 Tufton Street
London SW1P 3RB
Tel: 0171-222 5533
Fax: 0171-222 1591

An international organization concerned with the strengthening and preservation of marriage and Christian family life.

Infertility

British Pregnancy Advisory Service (BPAS)
Austy Manor
Wootton Wawen
Solihull
W Midlands B95 6BX
Tel: 01564-793225; 08457-304030 (Lo-call helpline)
Fax: 01564-794935

Provides help and advice to women faced with an unwanted pregnancy. Provides pregnancy testing, emergency contraception, male and female sterilization, cervical smears and a full abortion service, including counselling.

Child
Charter House
43 St Leonards Road
Bexhill-on-Sea
E Sussex TN40 1JA
Tel: 01424-732361
Fax: 01424-731858

Promotes improved care and treatment of infertility and provides information and support for people suffering from infertility, through teaching ways to overcome the problem. Runs a counselling and 24-hour telephone answering service.

Foresight Charity for Preconceptual Care
28 The Paddock
Godalming
Surrey GU7 1XD
Tel: 01483-427839
Fax: 01483-427668

Promotes optimal health in both parents before trying to conceive, to reduce the risk of handicap and to promote optimal health in the infant.

ISSUE - The National Fertility Association
114 Lichfield Street
Walsall
West Midlands
WS1 1SZ
Tel: 01922-722888
Fax: 01922-640070
e-mail: webmaster@issue.co.uk
Website: www.issue.co.uk

A national charity providing independent information, support and representation to people with fertility difficulties. A confidential evening telephone counselling service with professionally trained counsellors is available.

National Endometriosis Society (NES)
Suite 50
Westminster Palace Gardens
1-7 Artillery Row
London SW1P 1RL
Tel: 0171-222 2776 (crisis helpline 7-10pm)
Fax: 0171-222 2786

Promotes research into the causes of endometriosis and provides support and information for sufferers.

NEEDS (National Egg And Embryo Donation Society)
Human Fertilization and Embryology Authority (HFEA)
Paxton House
30 Artillery Lane
London E1 7LS
Tel: 0161 276-6000

Are you aged 18-35, healthy and willing to donate some of your eggs to help another woman become a mother? For further information, contact the King's Assisted Conception Unit on 0171-346 3158 (London area). If outside London, contact NEEDS (National Egg and Embryo Donation Society) on 0161-276 6000 for details of your nearest Assisted Conception Unit OR The Human Fertilization and Embryology Authority (HFEA) at Paxton House, 30 Artillery Lane, London E1 7LS.

Careers

Better Business
Active Information
Cribau Mill
Llanvair Discoed
Chepstow NP6 6RD
Tel: 01291-641 222
Fax: 01291 641 777
e-mail:info@homerun.co.uk
Website: www.better-business.co.uk

Helps businesses to prosper through a magazine specially written for people who want to make money while enjoying the freedom of working for themselves. Provides information on running a business and making it profitable.

Business and Professional Women UK Ltd (BPW)
23 Ansdell Street
London W8 5BN
Tel: 0171-938 1729
Fax: 0171-938 2037

Promotes a free and responsible society in which women take an active part in decision-making at all levels. Encourages co-operation and understanding amongst all women, worldwide.

Equal Opportunities Commission
Overseas House
Quay Street
Manchester M3 3HN
Tel: 0161-833 9244

Health and Safety Executive Information Centre
Broad Lane
Sheffield S3 7HQ
Infoline: 0541-545500
Website:
www.open.gov.uk/hse/hsehome.htm

Provides information on issues relating to health and safety at work, including regulations affecting new and expectant mothers.

National Group on Homeworking (NGH)
Office 26
30-38 Dock Street
Leeds LS10 1JF
Tel. 0113-245 4273
Fax: 0113-246 5616

Promotes increased awareness of homeworking issues and aims to alleviate poverty among homeworkers.

New Ways to Work (NWW)
309 Upper Street
London N1 2TY
Tel: 0171-226 4026 (helpline)
Fax: 0171-354 2978
e-mail: nww@dircon.co.uk

Promotes increased awareness of flexible work patterns, in order to encourage equal access to jobs for people who have caring and domestic responsibilities and for people with disabilities.

OWNBASE
Birchwood
Hill Road South
Helsby
Cheshire WA6 9PT
Tel: 01928-723 254
e-mail: ownbase@coleman.u-net.com
Website: http://www.ownbase.org.uk
The national association for home-based working.

Parents at Work
4-5 Beech Street
London EC2Y 8AD
Tel: 0171-628 3565; 0171-628 3578
(helpline Tues, Thurs 11am-1pm, 2-4pm)
Fax: 0171-628 3591

Provides information and advice about childcare provision.

Childcare

National Childminding Association (NCMA)
8 Masons Hill
Bromley BR2 9EY
Tel: 0181-464 6164, 0181-466 0200
(advice line Mon, Tues 2-4pm; Thurs 1-3pm)
Fax: 0181-290 6834

Works to improve the status and standards of childminding – the home-based daycare of young children. Runs a membership organization for childminders and others involved in daycare for young children.

National Children's Centre
Brian Jackson Centre
New North Parade
Huddersfield
W Yorkshire HD1 5JP
Tel: 01484-519988
Fax: 01484-435150

Works to increase awareness of issues connected with the care and upbringing of children in order to promote a better quality of life for the child.

National Council of Voluntary Child Care Organizations
Unit 4
Pride Court
80-82 White Lion Street
London N1 9PF
Tel: 0171-833 3319
Fax: 0171-833 8637

Works in partnership with families to promote the principles and practices on which social services for children, young people and families should ideally be based.

National Early Years Network
77 Holloway Road
London N7 8JZ
Tel: 0171-607 9573
Fax: 0171-700 1105

Promotes the interests of young children under eight and supports working with parents of young children. Leaflets available upon request.

Spurgeon's Child Care (SCC)
74 Wellingborough Road
Rushden
Northants NN10 9TY
Tel: 01933-412412
Fax: 01933-412010

A Christian organization that provides positive experiences and help for children, young people and families through community services, structured activity groups and daycare facilities for children.

Working for Childcare
77 Holloway Road
London N7 8JZ
Tel: 0171-700 0281
Fax: 0171-700 1105

Encourages the provision of childcare facilities to meet the needs of working parents and their children.

Working Mothers Assocation
– same address as above
Tel: 0171-700 5771.

Special Cases

British Agencies for Adoption and Fostering (BAAF)

Skyline House
200 Union Street
London SE1 0LY
Tel: 0171-593 2000
Fax: 0171-593 2001

Promotes the interests of children separated from their families by supporting adoption and fostering services.

Childlink

10 Lion Yard
Tremadoc Road
London SW4 7NQ
Tel: 0171-498 1933
Fax: 0171-498 1791

Places children for adoption in co-operation with local authorities and provides support and counselling for those involved.

National Foster Care Association (NFCA)

Leonard House
5-7 Marshalsea Road
London SE1 1EP
Tel: 0171-828 6266
Fax: 0171-357 6668

Works to improve the quality of foster care and to encourage co-operation between related child care organizations and self-help groups.

Parent-to-Parent Information on Adoption Services (PPIAS)

Lower Boddington
Daventry
Northants NN11 6YB
Tel: 01327-260295
Fax: 01327-263565

Provides support for adoptive parents and those considering adoption through a nationwide network of adoptive families.

London Lesbian and Gay Switchboard

PO Box 7324
London N1 9QS
Tel: 0171-837 7324 (helpline)
Fax: 0171-837 7300

Provides a national 24-hour information and counselling service for homosexual men and lesbians, and maintains up-to-date information on all aspects of HIV and/or AIDS.

Positively Women (PW)

347-349 City Road
London EC1V 1LR
Tel: 0171-713 0222; 0171-713 0444 (admin)
Fax: 0171-713 1020

Provides free, confidential support for women with HIV infection and AIDS. Works to reduce the prejudice that surrounds HIV infection and to ensure the special needs of women are not overlooked. Provides practical assistance to mothers with HIV and/or AIDS mothers who have children with HIV and/or AIDS.

Terrence Higgins Trust (THT)

52-54 Gray's Inn Road
London WC1X 8JU
Tel: 0171-242 1010 (helpline 12 noon-10pm); 0171-405 2381 (legal line Mon, Wed 7-9pm)
Fax: 0171-242 0121

Promotes increased understanding of HIV and AIDS. Runs a telephone helpline, provides one-to-one practical support and counselling for people with AIDS, their friends and their families.

Family Problems/ Break-Ups/Single Parents

Both Parents Forever
39 Cloonmore Avenue
Orpington
Kent BR6 9LE
Tel: 01689-854343

Works to help all parents, grandparents and children understand their rights following divorce, separation or care proceedings, and in child abduction cases, or dual nationality cases. Works to maintain a meaningful relationship with both parents, and helps them to claim their rights, amicably if possible, or through court proceedings if necessary.

Families Need Fathers
134 Curtain Road
London EC2A 3AR
Tel: 0171-613 5060; helpline 0990-502506
Fax: 0171-613 5060 (telephone first)

Works to explore ways to maintain a child's relationship with both parents following separation and divorce.

Family Rights Group (FRG)
The Print House
18 Ashwin Street
London E8 3DL
Tel: 0171-249 0008 (advice 1.30pm-3.30pm); 0800 731 1696
Fax: 0171-923 2683

Advises families with children in public care, involved in child protection procedures or receiving family support services. Provides information on family and childcare law and good practice.

Gingerbread
16-17 Clerkenwell Close
London EC1R 0AA
Tel: 0171-336 8183; 0171-336 8184 (advice line)
Fax: 0171-336 8185

Provides practical help, support and advice for lone parents and their children via a national network of local self-help groups.

Marriage Care
Clitherow House
1 Blythe Mews
Blythe Road
London W14 0NW
Tel: 0345-573921 (Mon-Thurs 3pm-9pm, local call rates)

Provides a confidential information and listening service for people facing difficulties within their marriage or close personal relationship. Information on fertility awareness available through its independent service, Fertility UK.

National Association for Maternal and Child Welfare Ltd (NAMCW)
1st Floor
40-42 Osnaburgh Street
London NW1 3ND
Tel: 0171-383 4117
Fax: 0171-383 4115

Promotes education in human development, childcare and family life. Research projects involving single parents and parenting are currently in progress.

One Parent Families
255 Kentish Town Road
London NW5 2LX
Tel: 0171-267 1361
Fax: 0171-482 4851

Works to improve the economic, legal and social position of one-parent families.

Single Parent Action Network (SPAN)
Millpond
Baptist Street
Easton
Bristol BS5 0YW
Tel: 0117-951 4231
Fax: 0117-935 5208
e-mail: spanuk.demon.co.uk

Supports the development of self-help groups for one-parent families, especially those living in disadvantaged circumstances.

Relate
Herbert Gray College
Little Church Street
Rugby
Warwickshire CV21 3AP
Tel: 01788-573241
Fax: 01788-535007
Website: www.relate.org.uk

Works to support marriage and family life by providing counselling and sex therapy for couples with relationship problems, at over 120 local centres nationwide.

Finance

Money Management Council
PO Box 77
Hertford
Herts SG14 2HW
Tel: 01992-503448
Fax: 01992-503448

Promotes a better understanding and increased self-help in personal and family money management.

National Association of Citizens Advice Bureaux (NACAB)
115-123 Pentonville Road
London N1 9LZ
Tel: 0171-833 2181
Fax: 0171-833 4371

Provides free, impartial and confidential advice to anybody on any subject, including social security benefits, housing, family and personal matters, financial advice and consumer complaints. Phone for your local CAB office details.

Lesbian parenting

Rights of Women
52 Featherstone St
London EC1Y 8RT
Tel: 0171-251 6576

Legal advice and policy development on lesbian mother issues.

Lesbian Information Service
PO Box 8
Todmorden
Lancashire OL14 5TZ
Tel: 0706-817 235

National agency publishing information for both lesbians and for voluntary and statutory sectors.

Albert Kennedy Trust
Unit 305A
16/16a Baldwin Gdns
London EC1N 7RJ
Tel: 0171-831 6562

Organization providing temporary sheltered accommodation (not official fostering), to gay teenagers (age 16-19).

Stonewall Parenting Group
16 Clerkenwell Close
London EC14 OAA
Tel: 0171-336 8860
Fax: 0171-336 8864
e-mail: info@stonewall.org.uk.
Lesbian and gay parenting rights group.

**Lesbian & Gay Fostering & Adoptive
Parents Group**
c/o BM Friend, London WC1N 3XX

LesBeWell
PO Box 4048
Kings Heath
Birmingham
Midlands B14 7EF
Tel: 0121-441 1580
*Provides information on lesbian health, produces
Dykenosis newsletter, runs workshops.*

Happy Families
PO Box 1060
Doncaster
Yorkshire DN6 9QE
Tel: 01302-702601
*Parent support group for lesbian, gay and
bisexual people.*

Further Reading

Balaskas, J, *Active Birth* (Thorsons).

Dr Brewer, S, *Planning a Baby? A complete guide to preconceptual care* (Vermilion)

Dr Brewer, S, *Super Baby: Boost your baby's potential from conception to year 1* (Thorsons)

Dr Club, E, & Knight, J, *Fertility: Fertility Awareness and Natural Family Planning* (David & Charles)

Dr Cooper, C, *Twins and Multiple Births – the essential parenting guide from pregnancy to adulthood* (Vermilion)

Horlick, N, *Can You Have it All?*, (Macmillan)

McFerran, A, *Motherland*, (Virago)

Olivier, S, *What Should I Feed My Baby?* (Weidenfeld & Nicolson)

Books About Lesbian and Gay Parenthood

Alpert, H, *We Are Everywhere, Writings By And About Lesbian Parents,* The Crossing Press, Freedom, California, 1988

Arnup, K, *Lesbian Parenting – Living With Pride And Prejudice,* Gynergy Books, Canada, 1995

Benkov, L, *Reinventing The Family – The Emerging Story Of Lesbian And Gay Parents,* Crown Publishers, NY, 1994

Bozett, Frederick W, *Homosexuality and the Family,* Harrington Park Press, NY, London, 1989

Clunis, DM and Green, GD, *The Lesbian Parenting Book – A Guide To Creating Families And Raising Children,* Seal Press, USA, 1995

Griffin, K and Mulholland LA, *Lesbian Motherhood in Europe,* Cassell, London, 1997

Harne, L, *Rights of Women, Valued Families –The Lesbian Mother's Legal Handbook,* The Women's Press, London, 1997

Jenness, A, *Families: A Celebration Of Diversity, Commitment, And Love*, Houghton Mifflin, 1990

Lesbian Information Service, *Lesbians Who Are Mothers Resource List*, LIS, PO Box 8, Todmorden, Lancashire OL14 5TZ; tel 01706-817235. Send £2.

Manasse, G, photographer and Swallow, J, *Making Love Visible – In Celebration Of Gay And Lesbian Families*, The Crossing Press, Freedom, CA, 1995

Martin, A, *The Guide To Lesbian And Gay Parenting*, Pandora, London, 1994

Patterson, Charlotte J, 'Special Issue: Sexual Orientation and Human Development', *Developmental Psychology*, January 1995, Volume 31, Number 1

Patterson, Charlotte J, 'Children of Lesbian and Gay Parents', *Child Development*, 1992, 63, 1025-1042

Pies, C, *Considering Parenthood*, Spinsters Book Company, San Francisco, CA, updated 1988

Pollack, S & J Vaughan *Politics Of The Heart, A Lesbian Parenting Anthology*, Firebrand Books, Ithaca, NY, 1987

Rafkin, L, *Different Mothers – Sons And Daughters Of Lesbians Talk About Their Lives*, Cleis Press, Pittsburgh, 1990

Saffron, L, *Challenging Conceptions, Planning A Family By Self Insemination*, Cassell, London, 1994

Saffron, L, *What about the Children? Sons and Daughters of Lesbian and Gay Parents Talk About their Lives*, Cassell, London, 1996

Tasker, F and Golombok, S, *Growing Up In A Lesbian Family – Effects On Child Development*, Guildford Press, New York, London, 1997

Weston, K, *Families We Choose – Lesbians, Gay, Kinship*, Columbia University, Press, NY, 1991

index

active birth movement 171

adoption 107-109, 210

   see also professional advice on: adoption,
     the need for more adopters

age and conception 139-41

alcohol 118-19

   and sperm 129

allergies (infants) 190

amniocentesis 164

antenatal care 99

antenatal tests: 159-60

   see also blood tests: routine, for foetal
     abnormality.

   see also tests (foetal cells)

   see also ultrasound

au pair 82-3

autism see professional advice on: autism

baby 9-10

   calculating due dates 145-46

   influencing the sex of 142-3

   pre-term and low birth weight 202-206

   questions to ask (pre conception) 13-20

   see also professional advice on: what
     potential parents should be aware of
     before having a baby

   see also gay parenting: the reality

   sleeping with 179-80

biological clock 13

birth:

   attendant/s 170

   attending 39-40

   home 168-69

   other options 169

   plans 172-3

   recording 176-77

   see also gay parenting: options for

   stages of 173-76

blood tests:

   routine 161

   for foetal abnormality 161-62

bottle-feeding 187-88

breast-feeding 177, 186

   and returning to work 186-87

career breaks 59-61

childcare 77-85, 90

childminder 84

chorionic villus sampling (CVS) 164

contraception 132-34, 190

   see also pill

cordocentesis 164

cot death see professional advice on:
     reducing the risk of cot death

covenant *see* trust fund
crèches *see* nurseries
crying 188

divorce 104-106, 217
DOMINO (domiciliary in and out) 169
drugs 124-25
   and sperm 129
   of abuse 125
   over-the-counter 124-25
   prescription 124

education:
   further 92
   private 91
   state 91
employers (attitudes to families) 63-66
employment breaks *see* career breaks
environmental pollutants 131-32
executors 106-107
exercise 119-20
   and sperm 129-30
   whilst pregnant 156-58
   pelvic floor 192-93

father:
   and attending the birth 39-40
   as a carer 80-81
   not wanting to be a 39
   see also gay parenting: potential
      fatherhood wanting to be a 37-39
fertile time of the month 137-38
   see also ovulation: predicting

financial:
   planning 90-94
   support for children 103
fostering 109-10
friends (child care) 81

gay parenting:
   adoption 215
   conception 150-53
   options for birth 178
   parental responsibility 111-12
   potential fatherhood 49-52
   potential motherhood 33-36
   sharing the work 74-5
   the reality 24
genetic counselling 131
guardian (appointing) 101-102

hair loss *see* pregnancy: hair loss after help
   77
HIV:
   and sperm 210
   positive 210
   see also professional advice: wanting to
      have a baby when you are HIV positive
hospital (options) 169
house-husband 45

infections:
   and sperm 130
   genito-urinary 122-24
   whilst pregnant 120-24
insemination *see* gay parenting: conception

insurance:
  health and dental 93-4
  life 93
  multiple birth 94

job sharing 67

legal:
  considerations (adoption, surrogacy and
    fostering) 107-110
  implications (marital status) 102-106
listeria 120-21

maternity
benefits 99-100
  leave 15-16, 53-55
  statutory rights 98-99
minerals see vitamins and minerals
miscarriage 200-202
  see also professional advice: coping with
    miscarriage
  see also sex: and miscarriage
mortgages 90-91
mother (not wanting to be a) 31
mothers:
  advice for potential 113-125
  and fathers/sons and daughters 31-32
  helps (child care) 81-82
motherhood:
  adjusting to 29-30
  life style changes 26-7
  see also gay parenting: potential
    motherhood

see also professional advice on: support for
  a good start, your first baby

nannies 83-4
nurseries 84-5

one-to-one (child birth) 169
ovulation:
  predicting 141
  see also fertile time of the month

pain relief 172
parent 10-12
pensions 95
pill 135-36
postnatal depression: 193-94
  see also professional advice on: postnatal
    depression, the pill and postnatal illness
pregnancy:
  and safety at work 55-6
  common ailments 159
  early signs of 143-44
  hair loss after 190-91
  illness during 167
  multiple 206
  see also professional advice on: multiple
    births
  planning second or subsequent 16-17
  previous termination of 143
  tests 144
  your rights during 167
premature menopause 197-200
prenatal stimulation 166-67

professional advice on:

a child needs two parents 23

adoption 211-12

autism 218-19

coming to terms with your child's sexuality 222-25

coping with an unusually gifted child 220-21

coping with miscarriage 203-4

healthy eating in pregnancy 157

multiple births 207

postnatal depression 195

reducing the risk of cot death 183-85

support for a good start (after birth) 181

the life of a working mother 60

the need for more adopters 213-14

the pill and postnatal illness 196

the pros and cons of working from home 73

wanting to have a baby when you are HIV positive 208-9

weaning your baby 189

what potential parents should be aware of before having a baby 21-22

why can't I conceive? 147-49

your first baby 28

property: 95,103

division of 107

relatives (child care) 81

responsibility:

legal (to child) 101-107

parental 103-4

see also gay parenting: parental responsibility

rest (during pregnancy) 158-59

sabbaticals 61

saving 91-92

separation 104-106, 217

sex life:

after the baby is born (men) 42-43

and your partner's pregnancy 40-42

sex:

after pregnancy 191

and childbirth 166

and infection 165-66

and miscarriage 165

determining the 31

how often 139

in pregnancy 164-65

sleep 190

smoking: 119

and cot death 183

and sperm 128-29

sperm:

count 138-39

donor 152-53

see also alcohol: and sperm

see also drugs: and sperm

see also HIV: and sperm

see also infections: and sperm

see also smoking: and sperm

temperature 126

stress 129

surrogacy 109

tax: 95
   children's personal allowance 96-7
termination for abnormality 202
testicles (examining) 130
tests (foetal cells) 163-64
toxoplasmosis 121-22
trust fund (setting up) 96

ultrasound 162-63

vitamins and minerals: 117-18
   for potential fathers 127
vitamin C 127-28
vitamin E 128

weaning 188
   see also professional advice on: weaning
    your baby
weight:
   and health 114-117
   and male fertility 131
   gain (during pregnancy) 155-56
wills: 95-96

making a 106-7
work: 59-61
   going back to 61-63
   legal implications 100-101
   the dilemma 56-57
   your rights at 98-101
working:
   annual hours 69
   fathers 43-45
   flexible arrangements 66-70
   flexitime 69-70
   from home 70-72
   see also professional advice on: the pros
    and cons of working from home
   full time 69-70
   part-time 66-67
   see also professional advice on: the life of a
    working mother
   term-time 68-69
   voluntary reduced time 68

zinc 128

staying in touch

The publishers would be happy to publish further relevant quotes in future editions of this book. If any reader has comments to make about *I want to have a Baby?*, or would like to share their own experiences, please feel free to write to the author at the publisher's postal address or e-mail kcathie@aol.com